Organic Chemistry
Laboratory Manual

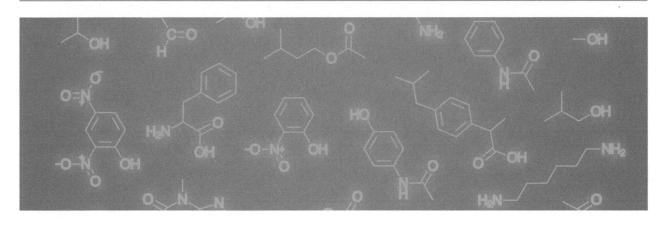

First Edition   Maciej J. Stawikowski

macmillan learning
curriculum solutions

Printed in the United States of America

10 9 8 7 6 5 4 3 2 1

ISBN 978-1-5339-0216-0

Macmillan Learning Curriculum Solutions
14903 Pilot Drive
Plymouth, MI 48170
www.macmillanlearning.com

Stawikowski 0216-0 W18

macmillan learning
curriculum solutions

Sustainability
Hayden-McNeil's standard paper stock uses a minimum of 30% post-consumer waste. We offer higher % options by request, including a 100% recycled stock. Additionally, Hayden-McNeil Custom Digital provides authors with the opportunity to convert print products to a digital format. Hayden-McNeil is part of a larger sustainability initiative through Macmillan Learning. Visit http://sustainability.macmillan.com to learn more.

bedford/st. martin's • hayden-mcneil
w.h. freeman • worth publishers

Contents

1. Course Overview

Course Objectives

The Organic Chemistry 1 and 2 Laboratory CHM2211L course objective is to become proficient with the research process and scientific method through:

- performing microscale synthesis of organic compounds using classic organic name and novel reactions;
- carrying out basic laboratory separation and preparative techniques (e.g.: solvent extraction, column chromatography, recrystallization, distillation, etc.)
- measuring of physical properties (e.g.: melting point, density) and characterizing prepared substances using various analytical techniques and instruments (e.g. TLC, IR and NMR spectroscopy);
- carrying out literature and internet searches to obtain chemical data;
- properly recording all activities of the laboratory experience into a research lab notebook;
- clearly writing-up and interpreting all observations and data obtained in each experiment;
- writing scientific communications.

Course Website

The course website can be found at http://canvas.fau.edu. There you can track your experimental and quiz grades and specific information related to this course. General information including printable copies of syllabus and any experiment/schedule changes can also be found at this web address. Canvas system is also accessible through the mobile app. It is your responsibility as the student to check this website at least twice per week for important notices from your instructors.

Teaching Assistants

You will meet your assigned Teaching Assistant (TA) at the first laboratory session. Remember that your TAs are not your personal tutors, but they will help you and guide you during laboratory sessions. Your TA will also have help sessions outside of lab time if needed (TA office hours' policy will be discussed during 1st laboratory).

2. Laboratory Rules, Regulations and Safety

General Safety Rules

Due to safety regulations, certain attire is required in Organic Chemistry Laboratory. In the first laboratory, you will be instructed on safety rules and regulations. You must adhere to the following rules:

- No student may work in a lab unless a TA or the Laboratory Director is ON DUTY.
- Safety glasses/goggle, long-sleeved lab coats and long pants must be worn at all times and students must be properly attired in the laboratory – you will be asked to leave if you fail to wear your safety glasses or come to lab inadequately attired. (Regular prescription glasses are NOT an adequate substitute). Long hair must be tied.
- No eating, drinking or smoking is permitted in the laboratory. (This means no food or drinks are brought into the lab or stored in the lab.)
- No cell phones, computers or photographic/video cameras are allowed in the labs.
- No student may perform an unauthorized experiment.
- Do not sit on the workbench.
- Never leave an experiment (in-progress) unattended.
- Any chemical which produces toxic vapors must be used in a fume hood. (Generally, if you find a chemical in the fume hood, use it in the fume hood)
- Wipe up spilled chemicals and bottle rings immediately including all drops and crystals.
- Open flames (Bunsen burners) are NOT to be used in the Organic Labs.
- Never pipette any liquid by mouth - use a rubber bulb or micropipette.
- Keep your lab bench and common areas clean and organized.
- Do not leave the lab until your bench, the hoods and the lab are clean and tidy. This includes Balance/instrument room as well.
- Be attentive to your experiment.
- Be well prepared before you come to the lab.
- Know what to do in case of emergency.
- Report all accidents to your TA immediately.
- Properly dispense all types of waste.

All accidents in the lab – broken glass, cuts, burns, fires, spills and any others must be reported to your instructor (TA) immediately! Emergency equipment is located in both PS 237 and PS 239 laboratories. This includes first aid kits, spill kits, fire extinguishers, emergency shower and eyewash stations. Your TA will show you locations of this equipment.

Material Safety Data Sheets (MSDS)

As in any chemical laboratory also in this course, you will be working with various toxic or dangerous chemicals. Certain safety precautions will be outlined in these printed instructions. However, it is your responsibility to familiarize yourself with properties of the chemicals by looking at their Material Safety Data Sheets (MSDS). For your convenience, a vast majority of MSDS files are posted in PDF format on course's website. Apart from physicochemical properties of chemical compounds, MSDS information may include instructions for the safe use and potential hazards associated with a particular material or product.

Your signature is required on the Safety Agreement and the Syllabus Agreement before you begin work in the organic laboratory. Please read each item on both agreements, attest to each by signing and submitting the form to your TA before performing the first experiment.

Safety Agreement
Organic Chemistry Laboratory CHML 2211

Before you are allowed to work in the Organic Chemistry Laboratory's you must sign and date this agreement and give it to your Teaching Assistant (TA).

When in the laboratory, I will adhere to the laboratory safety rules listed below. I will:
1. Wear approved chemical safety glasses or goggles at all times!
2. Follow the laboratory dress code as specified by Syllabus and safety training video.
3. Not wear sandals and open-toed shoes as they are not acceptable footwear in the laboratory.
4. Handle all equipment and chemicals in a safe and proper manner.
5. Label all containers! Substances in unlabeled containers will be removed from the lab.
6. Dispose of chemical wastes as directed by the TA.
7. Be prepared by reading and planning the experiment before coming to the lab.
8. Arrive at the laboratory on time.
9. Not enter the laboratory unless the TA or the Laboratory Director is present.
10. Not leave any experiments unattended.
11. Keep my work area neat, clean and well-organized.
12. Recap all reagent bottles with correct lid after use!
13. Not modify any experiment in any way without the TA's approval.
14. Take all precautions to avoid inhaling or ingesting chemicals.
15. Not eat or drink while in the laboratory or bring food or drink into the lab.
16. Use the fume hood whenever fumes or smoke are produced, or when instructed to do so.
17. Not pipette by mouth.
18. Not put anything into my mouth while working in the lab.
19. Wash my hands before leaving the lab.
20. Keep track of which items are hot and do not touch anything that is hot.
21. Know what to do in case of an accident.
22. Know where all safety equipment is and how to use it.
23. Immediately, inform my TA of any lab accident-no matter how small.
24. Keep all glassware, equipment, storage drawers clean.
25. Keep work bench, fume hood and other assigned common areas clean.
26. Properly and safely use any laboratory instrumentation.
27. Leave the laboratory clean.

I understand that it is my responsibility to familiarize myself with all safety regulations and to follow them at any given time when present in Organic Chemistry Laboratory. I understand that in any accident that is caused by my disobedience of rules and regulations, I am solely responsible for all consequences.

Printed name of student:_____

Signature of student:_____ _____Date:_____

3. Glassware

Glassware used in the course

In this laboratory, you will be issued with a set of glassware and other small equipment. Your personal glassware set will be kept in your locked drawer. You will check-in your glassware at the beginning of the semester and check it out at the end. The lab fee that you pay when registering for the course covers only the consumable/disposable items (reagents, solvents, pipets, gloves, etc.) and does not cover any glassware/equipment you break or loose throughout a semester. At the end of the semester you may be billed the replacement cost of any items missing from your drawer. Check everything during glassware check-in!

If you drop this course at any point during the semester, you must come back and check out your drawer. The failure to do so will result in a bill covering cost of all items in the drawer as if they all needed to be replaced.

How does it look?

Below you will find pictures of common lab glassware found in this laboratory. Pictures below will help you identify them.

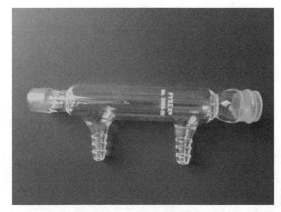

Jacketed reflux condenser

Air reflux condenser

Hickman still head

Erlenmeyer flasks

Claisen head

Drying tube

Craig recrystallization tube

1 ml, 3 mL, 5 mL conical vials

Magnetic spin vane

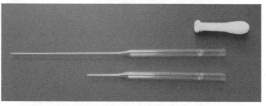

Long and short Pasteur Pipette and rubber bulb

Filtering flask

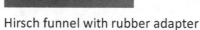

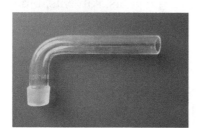

Spatula (top) and scoopula (bottom)

Hirsch funnel with rubber adapter

Large and small test tube

Beaker

Stirring rod

Note:
depicted glassware
is out of proportion

Organic Chemistry Laboratory CHM 2211L

Glassware check list/drawer inventory

Semester: _____

Section #: _____   Room: _____   Teaching Assistant: _____

Student name (printed): _____

Z #: _____   Drawer #: _____

Quantity	Description	check-in	check-out	comments
1	Jacketed Reflux Condenser	☐	☐	
1	Air Reflux Condenser	☐	☐	
1	Hickman Still Head	☐	☐	
1	Erlenmeyer Flask 10mL	☐	☐	
1	Claisen Head with cap and septum	☐	☐	
1	Drying Tube	☐	☐	
1	Craig recrystallization tube (2pcs set)	☐	☐	
1	1.0 mL Conical Vial with cap and septum	☐	☐	
1	3.0 mL Conical Vial with cap and septum	☐	☐	
1	5.0 mL Conical Vial with cap and septum	☐	☐	
1	Magnetic spin vane	☐	☐	
1	Pasteur pipette & rubber bulb	☐	☐	
1	25 mL filtering flask	☐	☐	
1	Hirsch filter funnel with rubber adapter	☐	☐	
1	stirring rod	☐	☐	
1	spatula	☐	☐	
1	small (13 x100 mm) test tube	☐	☐	
1	large (16 x 160 mm) test tube	☐	☐	
1	150 mL beaker	☐	☐	
1	400 mL beaker (or similar)	☐	☐	

READ & SIGN: I have accepted the DRAWER inventory issued to me and agree to reimburse FAU Deptartment of Chemistry and Biochemistry for any loss/breakage.

CHECK-IN

Student's signature:_____   Date:_____

CHECK-OUT

Student's signature:_____   Date:_____

4. Instrumentation and software

Instrumentation

In this laboratory, you will gain hands-on experience with a number of modern instrumentation. This will include nuclear magnetic resonance (NMR) spectrometer, Infrared (IR) spectrometer and melting point apparatus. In this chapter, you will find instrument description and step-by-step instructions on how to use it.

NMR Spectrometer

Organic chemistry laboratory is equipped with two benchtop Nuclear Magnetic Resonance (NMR) spectrometers. The 42.5 MHz Spinsolve Carbon® NMR spectrometer (Magritek, New Zealend) is shown on Figure 1. Spinsolve uses standard 5 mm OD NMR test tubes, exactly the same as high field instruments, so sample handling is familiar and convenient. Because there is no superconducting magnet, Spinsolve costs a fraction of traditional high field systems to purchase and requires no expensive ongoing cryogen refills. Only a standard mains power supply is required and it consumes no more power than a regular PC computer. The spectrometer is capable of monitoring ^1H, ^{19}F and ^{13}C nuclei. It can use various pulse sequences for 1D or 2D NMR techniques. The spectra acquisition software is called Spinsolve. For spectra processing we will use another piece of software: Mnova (Mestrelab Research, Spain). This software is capable of reading and processing (pick peaking, calibration, integration) of Spinsolve- acquired NMR spectra.

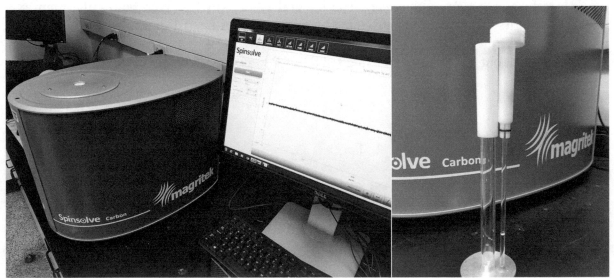

Figure 1. Spinsolve NMR spectrometer (A). To the right: sample holder with NMR tube (B).

NMR spectra acquisition instructions

Your TA will insert the NMR tube into NMR spectrometer for you. Once inserted, you may obtain your desired set of spectra.

A. Obtaining ^{1}H NMR spectra

In the SPINSOLVE software:
1. Click ^{1}H NMR mode.
2. Click ![PROTON] protocol. Select following parameters:
   a. Select deuterated solvent used from drop-down menu.
   b. Provide your **sample name**
   c. Select QUICKSCAN
3. Click [START] button to acquire your spectrum. It will take only 10 seconds!
4. After acquisition is complete you will transfer your spectrum to processing software called MNOVA. Click on ![MNOVA] icon to do it.

In the MNOVA software:
5. Your transferred ^{1}H NMR spectrum will be partially processed using built-in automatic functions. Your peaks will be labeled, integrated (automatically) and summarized for you. However, these automated algorithms may not be precise.
6. You have to perform a manual peak integration.
7. To manually integrate peaks, press "I" key on keyboard. The cursor will change from arrow to integral symbol $\int$. Now you will have to click left mouse button and drag it to select integration area around the peak. The integral value will be given below the ppm axis. Note: the first peak you choose to integrate will have a value of 1 unit. This can be changed, if necessary.
8. Please print out your spectrum using **CTRL + P** keyboard shortcut or press printer icon.

B. Obtaining ^{13}C NMR spectra

In the SPINSOLVE software:

1. Go to the main MENU. Click [MENU].
2. Click ^{13}C NMR mode.
3. Click ![CARBON] protocol. Select following parameters:

     a.   Solvent selection must be set to NONE.

     b.   Provide your **sample name**. It will be copied automatically from last (^{1}H in this case) experiment.

     c.   Select number of SCANS to be **64**.

4. The repetition time should be set to **2**.

5. Click ⬚START⬚ button to acquire your spectrum. Please wait as ^{13}C NMR spectra take much more time to acquire! You may start thinking of your ^{1}H NMR spectrum assignment already!

6. After acquisition is complete you will transfer your spectrum to processing software called MNOVA. Click on ⬚MNOVA⬚ icon to do it.

In the MNOVA software:

7. Your transferred ^{13}C NMR spectrum will be partially processed using built-in automatic functions. Your peaks will be labeled automatically. ^{13}C NMR spectra are note being integrated.

8. If your peaks are not labelled/integrated correctly, please ask you TA for help.

9. Please print out your spectrum using **CTRL + P** keyboard shortcut or press printer icon.

All spectra acquisition parameters are experiment specific. Please consult your TA before running any measurements.

Infrared (IR) Spectrometer

This laboratory is equipped with two Nicolet iS5 FT-IR Spectrometers (Thermo Fisher Scientific, USA) to acquire IR spectra of organic compounds (Figure 2).

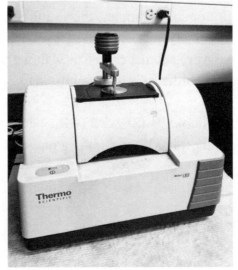

Figure 2. Nicolet iS5 FT-IR Spectrometer

     Infrared spectroscopy is based on the interaction between energy from the incident IR light and the covalent bonds within a molecule. In infrared spectroscopy, the frequency of light impinging on the molecule must be identical to the natural frequency of the molecular vibrations. The natural frequency of this resonance is based on a number of factors, including the mass of the atoms in the bond and the bond order. The vibration of the bond must also cause a change in the dipole moment of the molecule in order for the infrared light to be absorbed. The advantage of an FT-IR (Fourier-transform infrared) spectrometer is that all wavelengths of light are measured simultaneously, allowing for a much shorter analysis time compared to traditional dispersive instruments. For this type of analysis to be possible, the light from the source must pass through a precise optical component before it reaches the sample. This optical device is known as an interferometer and is used to generate an interference pattern in the wavelengths of light emitted from the source. The interference pattern is based on the movement of an internal mirror and is later mathematically altered via the Fourier transform function to produce the recognizable FT-IR spectrum. To collect the spectrum for a sample, the instrument first measures the intensity of each wavelength of light with no sample present in the beam path. This spectrum is referred to as the background. When the sample is inserted into the beam path, some of the infrared light from the source is absorbed by the covalent bond vibrations within the molecule. The instrument collects the sample spectrum and uses a ratio to eliminate the background spectrum from the equation, leaving behind a spectrum that is unique to the sample components. Much like chemical shift correlations in NMR spectroscopy determine the chemical structure of a molecule, characteristic infrared light absorption frequencies in infrared spectroscopy determine chemical functional groups present within a molecule.

Attenuated Total Reflection (ATR) is the most popular sampling technique for FT-IR analysis (Figure 3). ATR has supplanted transmission analysis for many applications due to its ease of use and minimal sample preparation. The depth of penetration of infrared light into the sample is on the order of a few micrometers. Therefore, it is critical for samples to be in intimate contact with the ATR crystal. For solid samples, this requires pressing the sample into the crystal using a pressure device. Common crystals used in ATR include ZnSe, Ge and diamond. ZnSe is a good and relatively inexpensive crystal that can be used down to 550 cm^{-1}, but it is somewhat soft and tends to scratch. Ge is much harder so is more robust than ZnSe and is useful to about 650 cm^{-1}.

In our laboratory, the Nicolet™ iS™ 5 FT-IR Spectrometer is equipped with laminated diamond crystal allowing for recording IR spectra in a range of 4,200 - 650 cm^{-1}.

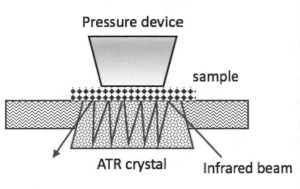 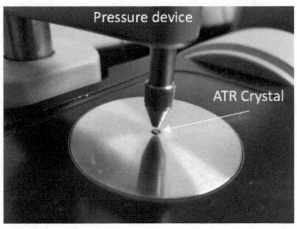

Figure 3. ATR technique. The incoming light is focused through the crystal onto the sample/crystal interface. Some light is absorbed by the sample. Unabsorbed light is reflected out of the ATR crystal to the detector. Photograph on the right shows ATR crystal of Nicolet FT-IR Spectrometer.

Recording of IR spectra is very simple. Nicolet iS5 FT-IR Spectrometer uses OMNIC® software to record and analyze IR spectra. Below you will find detailed instructions on how to use it. The following process is available also as a video tutorial.

IR spectra recording and processing using OMNIC software

Double click the **OMNIC** desktop icon.
1. Log in as **STUDENT.**
2. Make sure the pressure device, is not in contact with the crystal (Figure 3). Clean the crystal with cotton pad and methanol.
3. In the upper left hand corner of the screen from the menu bar, select **COLLECT BACKGROUND.**
4. Confirmation box will appear, select **OK**
5. In the upper right hand corner select **START COLLECTION.** Background will start to collect and you can see the progress of the background being collected in the lower left hand corner of screen (8 scans).
6. Confirmation box will appear, select **NO**
7. Place the sample on the crystal and apply pressure by rotating the knob clockwise until maximum pressure is reached. Make sure when placing sample, you cover the entire crystal. When you have tightened the knob to its maximum value the control clicks. **NO** pressure is needed for liquids.
8. In the upper left hand corner select **COLLECT SAMPLE.**
9. Collect sample window will appear, Enter the spectrum title: **Last Name, First Name and Date** (example Doe, John 9.8.11) then select **OK.**

10. Confirmation box will appear, Select **OK**
11. In the upper right hand corner of the screen from the menu bar, select **START COLLECTION.** You will notice in the lower left hand corner of screen the progress of the scans are shown. (8 scans)
12. When the collection stops, a window appears, select **YES** to confirm and Add to window.

13. Bottom of the left hand corner of screen select the symbol **T** . This will allow you to manually choose the peaks on the spectrum. Use the arrow to select the peaks in which you will identify. Alternatively, you may want to use **FIND PEAKS** icon to select all peaks automatically and then click REPLACE spectrum icon.

14. After selecting peaks, the bottom left hand corner of screen, select the symbol
15. Select **PRINT** from the menu bar at the top left hand corner of screen. Print window will appear select **PRINT**.
16. Exit out of screen by selecting the **"X"** in the upper right hand corner of screen.
17. Confirmation box will appear select **NO** to save changes.
18. Clean the crystal with cotton pad and methanol.
19. Dispose of waste in correct location.

Melting point analysis

The melting point of a substance is the temperature at which the material changes from a solid to a liquid state. Pure crystalline substances have a clear, sharply defined melting point. During the melting process, all of the energy added to a substance is consumed as heat of fusion and as a result, the temperature remains constant throughout the phase transition. Determining the melting point is a simple and fast method used in many diverse areas of chemistry to obtain a first impression of the purity of a substance. This is because even small quantities of impurities change the melting point or at least clearly enlarge its melting range.

The determination of melting points is one of the oldest identification and test methods for organic substances. The melting point is easy to measure, tabulate and classify. Extensive collections of tables give the exact values of many pure compounds. The primary requirement for a good melting point determination is that the sample be in a fine powder form. This assures efficient and reproducible heat transfer into the sample and enhances the overall appearance of the sample for easier detection of the melt. Coarse crystalline and non-homogeneous samples must be crushed into a fine powder in a mortar.

For the melting point determination, you will use the MPA160 melting point apparatus capable of measuring melting points in a range of 50°-260°C (Figure 5). Please familiarize yourself with this instrument.

Figure 4. Melting point apparatus MPA160 used in our laboratory. Description: 1- cowl, 2- oven cover, 3- lens, 4- keypad, 5- tube tapper.

Sample preparation

Your TA will demonstrate you how to load your sample into a capillary tube. Any substance being loaded into a melting point capillary must be (1) fully dry, (2) homogeneous and (3) in powdered form. To fill a capillary tube with a sample, the open end of the capillary is pressed gently into the substance several times. The powder is then pushed to the bottom of the tube by repeatedly tapping the bottom of the capillary against a hard surface. The integral tube tapper in DigiMelt does this very well. Place each capillary in the molded form on the chassis (see Figure 4). Press the tube tapper button and your samples will be packed. If desired the tube tapping sequence may be repeated. Alternatively, the capillary tube can be dropped onto a table through a glass/plastic tube of ~1 m in length.

A sample height between 2 and 3 mm is recommended in the DigiMelt for optimum results and reproducibility.

The sample tubes are loaded into the DigiMelt by inserting them into one of the sample position slots located on top of the instrument. Up to three samples can be accommodated by the heating block. Never force a capillary into the heating block!

Melting point of a substance relates to compound's purity. Roughly, a 1% of a foreign substance will result in a 0.5 °C depression. This is the main reason why a melting point range is the preferred record of a melting point determination, and is more useful than a single temperature report.

Recording melting point using DigiMelt apparatus

Initial Digimelt settings (step 1 – 6) will be prepared by your TA

1) Push **Start Temp** and use the ↑/2 and ↓/3 buttons to set the starting temperature (generally 5 degrees below the expected melting point).

2) Push **Ramp Rate** and use the ↑/2 and ↓/3 buttons to set the ramp rate (2 deg/min is suggested).

3) Push **Stop Temp** and use the ↑/2 and ↓/3 buttons to set the stop temperature (at least 5 degrees

above the expected melting point).

4) Push **Stop Temp** again to return to the current temperature display.

5) Push **Start/Stop** to preheat the block to the starting temperature. The **Preheat** LED will light.

6) When the **Ready** LED becomes lit, the oven is holding at the start temperature.

7) Load capillaries with sample.

(OPTIONAL STEP: Insert capillaries into the chassis holes near the Tube Tapper button)

Press the **Tube Tapper** button to pack your samples

8) Insert your samples into the DigiMelt oven.

9) Push **Start/Stop** to begin ramping the temperature at the ramp rate. The **Melt** LED will light.

10) Observe your samples during the ramp.

11) Push the 1, ↑/2 and ↓/3 buttons to record data (up to 4 temperatures per sample) during the melt.

(To end the experiment before the stop temperature is reached, push the **Start / Stop** button.)

12) When the **Cooling** LED is lit, the experiment is over. If you recorded data, the **Data** LED is also lit.

13) To read back the data, push the 1, ↑/2 and ↓/3 buttons (make sure the **Cooling** LED is lit).

Please watch a video tutorial on how to prepare sample and run melting point determination experiment.

Chemical Drawing Software

In this course, you will use chemical drawing software - Chemdoodle. This software is available for you for free. Please visit http://www.chemdoodle.com/ to download and install it. It is available for MS Windows, Linux and OS X operating systems. Detailed instructions on how to download and install this software are available on the course website (Canvas).

Chemdoodle can be used for:
- Drawing reaction schemes, reaction mechanisms,
- Naming of your structures using IUPAC conventions,
- Drawing glassware,
- Drawing TLC plates,
- Prediction of ^1H and ^{13}C NMR spectra of drawn compounds,
- Calculation of many physicochemical properties including molecular weight.

There is a learning curve to be able to use it efficiently. It is highly recommended that you install this software and start using it at the beginning of the semester!

Reference manager

During writing your laboratory reports you will be required to cite scientific literature. Although MS Word can help you with that, it is highly recommended that you use a reference manager software. When writing scientific reports, it is important to use proper literature sources. Common websites – such as other universities course ones are not valid sources! Please use peer reviewed journals and books as reference.

It is highly recommended that you familiarize yourself with reference managing software. It really facilitates literature citing process and ensures that proper formatting is in place.

One of the best (freely available) reference managers is Mendeley Desktop. Mendeley can import references from journals, databases etc. It is also compatible with MS Word (OSX & Windows) – runs as a plugin. For more info on how to install Mendeley and use it please visit: https://www.mendeley.com/downloads

You will be asked to create free account, and will be able to use the software even in online mode. After installation, a screen will show you how to install Microsoft Word plugin:

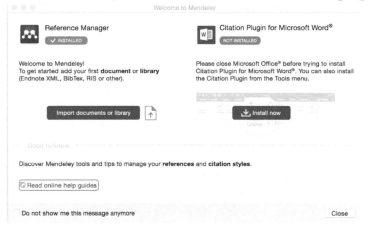

After successful installation, you will find Mendeley plugin under **References** tab:

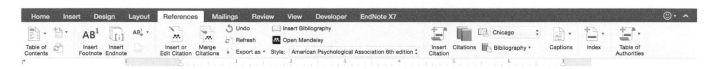

Using Mendeley is very intuitive. Unfortunately, this software is not supported by FAU's IT department nor any personnel involved in the course. Mendeley has many good quick tutorials (text, video) available on their website: https://community.mendeley.com/guides.

You can add references manually or search for your citations using Literature search box:

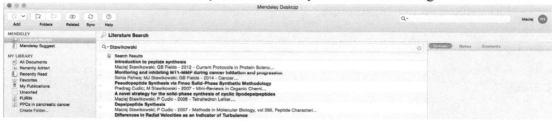

You can also import it from publisher's websites or Google Scholar. The citation styles can also be customized. They are found under **View > Citation Styles > More styles**:

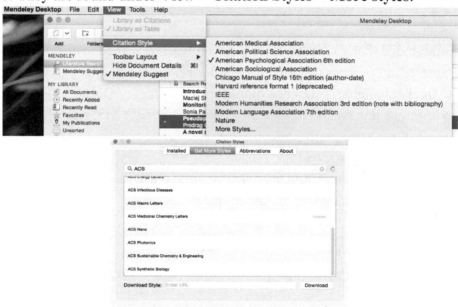

The ACS Medicinal Chemistry Letters style is to be used for this lab report purposes.

Using Reference manager in your reports really helps![1]

(1)   Liu, M.; Sibi, M. P. Recent Advances in the Stereoselective Synthesis of B-Amino Acids. *Tetrahedron* **2002**, *58* (40), 7991–8035.

5. Essential Laboratory Techniques

In this chapter, you will find basic information on essential laboratory techniques used in this course. Many of the techniques described here are included in the video tutorials available on course website (Canvas).

Recrystallization

Crystallization is the most important method for the purification of solid organic compounds. A crystalline organic substance is made up of a three-dimensional array of molecules held together by specific intermolecular interactions. Most crystallizations in the laboratory is carried out by dissolving the material to be purified in the appropriate hot solvent. As the solvent cools, the solution becomes saturated with respect to the substance, which then crystallizes. As the perfectly regular array of a crystal is formed, foreign molecules are excluded and thus the crystal is one, pure substance. Soluble impurities stay in the solution because they're not concentrated enough to saturate the solution. The crystals are collected by filtration, the surface of the crystals is washed with small amount of <u>cold</u> (important!) solvent to remove the adhering impurities and then crystals are dried.

The process of crystallization contains the following steps:
1. Choosing the appropriate solvent for your compound (soluble in hot, sparsely soluble in cold).
2. Dissolving the solute (may require heating).
3. Removing suspended solids (typically Pasteur filter pipet is used).
4. Crystalizing the solute.
5. Collecting and washing of the crystals (Hirsch funnel filtration).
6. Drying of the product.

Filtration using Hirsch funnel

Hirsch[1] funnels are essentially smaller Büchner funnels and primarily used to separate a desired solid from a relatively small volume of liquid (1-10 mL). The main difference is that the plate is much smaller, while the walls of the funnel angle outward instead of being vertical. Your typical setup for Hirsch funnel filtration is depicted on Figure 5. Metal block is used to hold the setup in place. Alternatively, a laboratory stand may be used. Hirsch funnel filtration technique is presented

---

[1] Robert Hirsch, German chemist (1856-1913).

in video tutorial available on Canvas. Hirsch funnels must be used in conjunction with external vacuum source to filter off the solids.

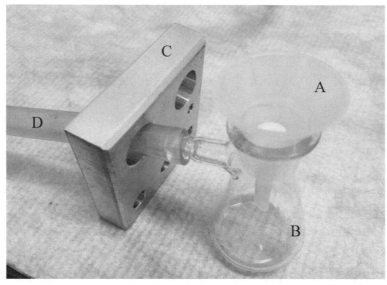

Figure 5. Hirsch funnel filtration set-up. A) Hirsch funnel, B) Erlenmeyer flask, C) metal block, D) vacuum hose

Thin Layer Chromatography

Thin-layer chromatography (TLC) is a fast, sensitive and inexpensive analytical technique that is commonly employed in organic laboratory. As little as 10^{-9} g of material can be detected, although the usual sample size is $1 - 100$ μg.

TLC involves spotting the sample to be analyzed near one end of the sheet of glass/plastic/aluminum sheet coated with a thin layer of an adsorbent. The sheet is then placed in a covered jar containing a shallow layer of solvent. As solvent raises by capillary action up through the adsorbent, differential partitioning occurs between the components of the mixture dissolved in the solvent and the stationary adsorbent phase. The more strongly a given component of the mixture is adsorbed onto the stationary phase, the more slowly it will migrate up the TLC plate.

TLC is commonly used for:
1. **To determine the number of components in a mixture.**
   Knowing the number and relative amounts of the components helps in planning of further purification steps.
2. **To determine the identity of the substance.**
   If two substances spotted on the same TLC plate give spots in identical locations, they *may* be identical. If the spot positions are not the same, the substances cannot be the same.

3. **To monitor the progress of the reaction.**
   By sampling reaction from time to time it is possible to watch the reactants disappear and products appear using TLC.

4. **To determine the effectiveness of a purification.**
   The effectiveness of distillation, crystallization, extraction and other techniques can be monitored using TLC.

5. **To determine the appropriate conditions for a column chromatographic separation.**
   The correct adsorbent and solvent system used to carry out the column chromatography can be determined quickly by TLC.

6. **To monitor column chromatography separation.**
   As column chromatography is carried out the eluted solvent is collected in a number of small flasks/tubes (fractions). To verify that the desired product is collected from appropriate fractions a TLC analysis is performed.

The two most common coatings for TLC plates are alumina (Al_2O_3) and silica gel (SiO_2). The same adsorbents are most commonly used for column chromatography as well.

Common solvents used in chromatography are listed in Table 1. In general, those solvents are characterized by a low boiling points and low viscosities that allow them to migrate more rapidly. Often times, two different solvents are used in various proportions to fine-tune the polarity of the mixture which is the average of the two.

Table 1. Common chromatography solvents and their relative polarities

Solvent	Relative polarity
Petroleum ether	*most non-polar*
Hexanes	
Diethyl ether	
Dichloromethane	
Ethyl acetate	
Acetone	
2-propanol	
Ethanol	
Methanol	
Water	
Acetic acid	*most polar*

The order in which solutes migrate on TLC is the same as the order of solvent polarity. Figure 6 shows relative order of solute migration.

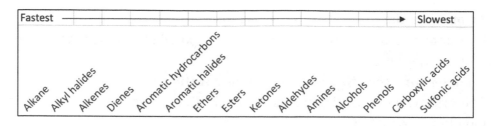

Figure 6. Relative order of solute migration

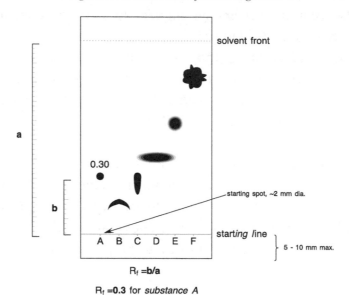

$R_f = b/a$

$R_f = 0.3$ for *substance A*

Figure 7. TLC plate. Lanes A-F show typical spot shapes observed. Lane A represents the ideal spot shape.

The identity of the sample on a TLC plate is characterized by its retention factor (R_f) value (Figure 7).

The R_f value is the ratio of the distance the center of the spot travels from the point of origin to the distance the solvent travels. It ranges from 0 to 1 and has no units.

The spots can only be observed when colored substances are present. When colorless compounds are analyzed, a fluorescent indicator containing TLC plate must be used. When such TLC sheet is placed under 254 nm ultraviolet light, spots that quench the fluorescence can be seen.[2] Additionally, a number of other substances/solutions can be used to visualize spots on TLC. These specialized spray reagents have been developed that give specific colors for certain types of compounds.

---

[2] Please do not look directly at UV light as it will damage your eyes. Always use the appropriate UV filter.

The typical TLC procedure is as follows. Appropriate size, pre-cut TLC plate must be used.

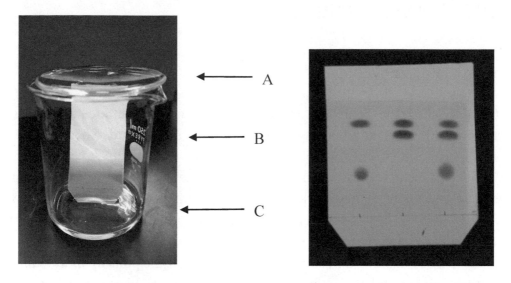

Figure 8. Typical TLC chamber (left picture). A) watch glass, B) beaker C) solvent line. Please note trimmed bottom edges of the plate and solvent line – below starting line. Plate visualized under UV lamp (right picture)

Alternatively, the plate can be cut out from the larger TLC plate sheet. Next, using a soft pencil the starting line is drawn ~10 mm from the bottom end of the plate.[3] Your starting line must be drawn above level of solvent in the chamber! After that a number of marks are made on the starting line corresponding to the number of different samples to be run (A, B, C, or 1,2,3… etc.). Solution of the sample to be analyzed is spotted onto the starting spot marks. Spotting must be performed quickly because the longer the capillary tube is in contact with the TLC plate the larger the starting spot becomes. The ideal spot size is around 2 mm in diameter. To be sure that you have put enough material on TLC plate you may want to look at it under UV light (if the plates contains a fluorescent indicator). Once your solution has been properly spotted, you have to wait a little moment so that the solvent used to dissolve your sample is evaporated.[4] After that the plate is inserted into a beaker or jar containing small amount of a solvent.[5] Your starting spot must be above the solvent line. Upon plate insertion, the top (cap or watch glass) is put in place (Figure 8). The solvent travels rapidly up in the thin layer by capillary action. Once the solvent line reaches the desired level (usually 5-10 mm from the top of the plate) one can remove the plate from the jar and quickly mark the front, before the solvent evaporates. Next, plate is air-dried (under the fume hood) and visualized under a UV light. All spots are circled (under a UV light) with pencil immediately after plate development and R_f values can be then calculated.

---

[3] Make sure you do not destroy the fragile adsorbent layer! Pencil must be soft (N° 2, non-mechanical)
[4] If you don't do that your spots will smear (example: Figure 8, spot C).
[5] Plate must be held by the edges. Never touch the surface of the adsorbent!

Column chromatography

Column chromatography is one of the most useful methods for the separation and purification of both solids and liquids when carrying out small scale experiments.

The theory of column chromatography is analogous to that of thin layer chromatography. The adsorbents are the same (silica gel, alumina, etc.) The sample is dissolved in a small quantity of the solvent (eluent) and applied at the top of the column. The eluent flows down through the column filled with adsorbent. Just as in TLC, there is an equilibrium established between the solute adsorbed on silica gel and the eluting solvent flowing down through the column. The three mutual interactions must be considered in column chromatography: the polarity of the sample, the polarity of the eluting solvent and the activity of the adsorbent. All these interactions will influence separation of your mixture on the column.

Uniform packing of the chromatography column is critical to the success of this technique. The sample is applied as a very concentrated solution in the solvent that will dissolve it best. As elution takes place, this narrow band of sample will separate into several bands corresponding to the number of components in the mixture and their relative polarities. It is essential that the components move through the column as a narrow horizontal band in order to come off the column in the least volume of solvent and not overlap with other components of the mixture. Therefore, the column should be vertical and the packing should be perfectly uniform, without voids caused by air bubbles. The preferred method for packing silica gel column is the slurry method, whereby a slurry of the adsorbent and the first eluting solvent is made and poured into the column. **It is extremely important to never let the column run dry at any time.** If it happens, it will allow air to enter the column, which will result in uneven bands and poor chromatographic separation. Your column chromatography set-up is shown on Figure 9.

Column packing

Prepare the column by packing it with a small cotton plug at the bottom of it. Next add small amount of sand so that it forms 5-10 mm layer. Make sure that the column's valve is closed and fix it on a laboratory stand. While stirring the silica slurry, pour it through the funnel into the column (make sure that you don't overfill it). Open the bottom valve and let the solvent drip to a beaker containing the slurry reservoir.

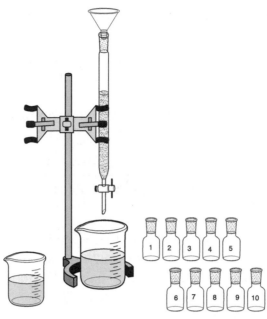

Figure 9. Column chromatography setup.

You will recycle the solvent so that all the silica slurry is transferred to the column. The silica gel will be settling down. Tap the column gently from the side using a spatula to help the silica to settle. Once the solvent level is approximately 1 inch above the settled silica gel level stop the flow and transfer the remaining slurry again on the top of the column, and open the valve to let it drip (but collect the solvent!). Continue slurry pouring/solvent recycling until all silica is transferred to the column. Once it's done, a 10 mm layer of the solvent must remain at the top of the column. Next, using a funnel, pour 5-10 mm layer of sand. Tap the column from the side to let it settle. Add another portion of the starting solvent and let it run through the column. Reduce the top layer of the remaining solvent to only 2-3 mm above the sand level (do not let the column run dry). At this point your column is packed and ready for use.

Extraction

Mixtures of compounds can be separated in many ways. In organic chemistry, liquid extraction (apart from filtration) is one of the most useful techniques used for product purification or isolation. Solvent extraction is a method to separate compounds based on their relative solubilities in two different immiscible liquids, usually water and an organic solvent. In other words, it is extraction of a compound from one liquid into another liquid phase. When a substance is mixed with a mixture of two immiscible solvents (for example water and ether), this substance will be distributed between the two phases –an equilibrium will be present. Some of it will dissolve in water and some in organic solvent:

$$Substance_{\,solvent\,1} \leftrightarrow Substance_{\,solvent\,2}$$

Partition coefficient (P) is the ratio of concentrations of a compound in a mixture of two immiscible phases at equilibrium:

$$P = \frac{C_2}{C_1} \quad \text{(unit is dimensionless)}$$

If concentration is expressed as g/100 mL then the partition coefficient is defined as:

$$P = \frac{(^g/_{100\ mL})\ organic\ layer}{(^g/_{100\ mL})\ water\ layer}$$

In medicine and medicinal chemistry, the partition coefficient is traditionally measured for 1-octanol/water ($K_{oct/wat}$) system. This information is useful to estimate distribution of drugs within the body. Hydrophobic drugs (high K values) will be mainly distributed in hydrophobic areas such as lipid bilayers. Conversely, hydrophilic compounds (low K values) will be found in aqueous environment such as blood serum.

Liquid extraction is typically performed using separatory funnel (see Figure 10). Using separatory funnel is not complicated. However, there are some important questions that must be answered before you proceed:

-   Does the stopper fit?
-   Is the stopcock assembled correctly? Does it leak?
-   Are there any cracks or sharp edges?
-   Is the separatory funnel large enough (it should be twice the total volume of the liquids used)?

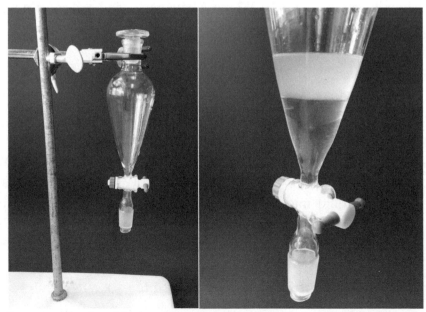

Figure 10. Separatory funnel used for liquid extraction. Separation of two immiscible layers (water/organic).

Pipetting using micropipettes and Pasteur pipettes

Micropipettes

Micropipettes are used to transfer small amounts (< 1 ml) of liquids. These are very expensive and delicate instruments. They are offered in different sizes, depending on the maximum volume of dispensing, expressed in microliters (µL). The scale on micropipettes is expressed in microliters. The value labeled on the micropipette shows the maximum volume (or volume range) in microliters that can be transferred with that size. Micropipettes are used in conjunction with *disposable* plastic tips.

The following is an illustration of a micropipette and its use (Figure 11 and 12):

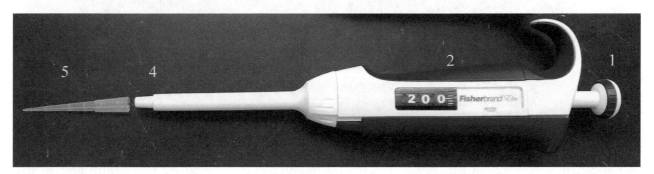

Figure 11. The structure of micropipette. 1 – plunger, 2 – volume display, 3 - tip discarding mechanism, 4 - discharge point, 5- plastic, disposable tip.

POSITION 1:	POSITION 2:	POSITION 3:	POSITION 4:

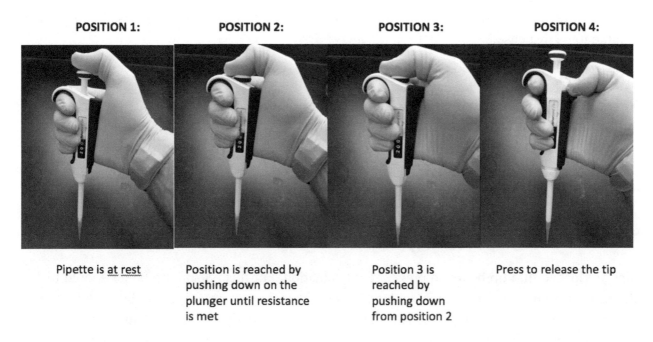

Pipette is <u>at rest</u>   Position is reached by pushing down on the plunger until resistance is met   Position 3 is reached by pushing down from position 2   Press to release the tip

Figure 12. Proper use of the micropipette

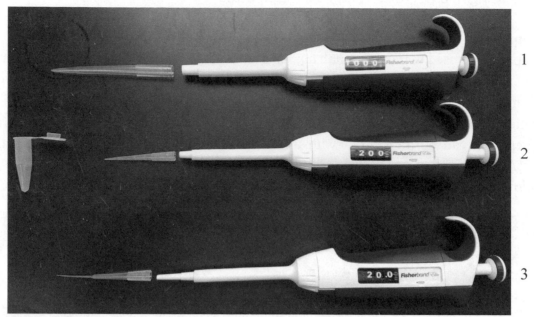

Figure 13. Various micropipettes. 1) 100 -1000 µL, 2) 20-200 µL, 3) 2-20 µL and the corresponding disposable plastic tips. Eppendorf tube shown to the left.

Micropipettes operate on the same principle: a plunger is depressed by the thumb and as it is released, liquid is drawn into a disposable plastic tip. When the plunger is pressed again, the liquid is dispensed.

The tips are an important part of the micropipette and allow the same device to be used for different samples (so long as you change your tip between samples) without washing. They come in a number of different sizes and colors, depending on the micropipette they are used with, and the volume to be dispensed.

IMPORTANT
Never hold the micropipette in horizontal or upside-down position as this will transfer the liquid inside the micropipette and will damage it!

The most commonly used tips are:
Large blue/white: 200-1000µL
Small yellow: 2-200µL
Small white: < 2µL

Tips are loaded into tip boxes to prevent contamination. For this reason, tip boxes should be kept closed if they are not in use. Tips are loaded onto the end of the micropipette by pushing the end of the device into the tip and giving two sharp taps. Once used, tips are ejected into special disposal bin located under the fume hood using the tip eject button. Never touch the tip with your fingers, as this poses a contamination risk.

IMPORTANT:

Some micropipettes deliver fixed volumes; however, the majority are adjustable. Each brand uses a slightly different method to do this. All have a readout which tells you how much is being delivered and a range of volumes which can be dispensed (Figure 14). Trying to dispense less than the lower value of the range will result in inaccurate measurements. Trying to dispense over the upper range will completely fill the tip and allow liquid to enter the body of the pipette.

Do not overwind the volume adjustment, as this affects the calibration of the micropipette!

Allowed range of volumes!

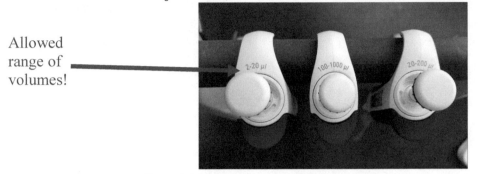

Figure 14. Micropipettes with adjustable volume.

NEVER CHANGE THE PRE-SET VOLUME OF THE MICROPIPETTE. YOUR TA WILL DO IT FOR YOU IF NECESSARY.

Pasteur pipettes

Pasteur pipettes are used to transfer small quantities of liquids. They are usually glass tubes tapered to a narrow point, and fitted with a rubber bulb at the top (Figure 15). They are named after the French scientist Louis Pasteur who used them in his research.

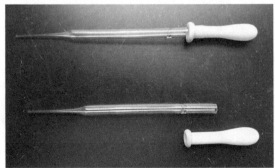

Figure 15. Pasteur pipettes and rubber bulbs.

Pasteur pipettes are commonly used in laboratories to transfer small amounts of liquids and in general they're disposable. Empty and used pipettes must be placed into broken glass boxes. The rubber bulbs are reusable.

IMPORTANT

Never hold the Pasteur pipette in horizontal or upside-down position as this will transfer the liquid inside the rubber bulb! It will cause rubber bulb contamination and organic solvents may dissolve the plastic bulb and cause spillage/accident!

6. Laboratory notebook

Laboratory notebook

The purpose of your laboratory notebook is to record all information regarding your practices in the laboratory. Everything that you record in your laboratory notebook must be entered in ink (not pencil!) and never deleted. All entries should be dated and signed.

Your laboratory notebook should contain all information necessary for someone else to carry out the experiment without looking for additional information elsewhere (additional literature). It should contain at least the following:

- Date
- Title of the experiment
- Summary information about experiment to be performed
- Balanced chemical equations, reaction mechanisms, if applicable
- Table of chemicals that includes physicochemical data and quantities for all chemicals used
- Drawings of glassware or instrumentation used
- Flowchart showing experimental procedures
- Detailed experimental procedures and observations carried out in the lab
- Experimental results, spectral analysis
- Experiment conclusion(s)
- Your signature

Your laboratory notebook serves as a place where a rough record of your experimental method/approach is documented. In other words, keeping a good laboratory notebook will help you to write a laboratory report or help others to repeat the experiment, if necessary!

Pre-lab preparation

You are required to come prepared for the laboratory. This means that before each laboratory session you must:

- Pay attention to the Canvas announcements
- Study chemistry concepts and laboratory techniques used in a particular experiment
- Read and understand given experimental procedures
- Watch tutorial videos (when applicable) showing more difficult experimental procedures
- **Write pre-lab information into your laboratory notebook**
- Answer additional pre-lab questions assigned by the instructor
- When instructed, take required quiz before lab session.

Pre-lab writing expectations

If not instructed otherwise, every pre-lab information entered into your laboratory notebook must include:

- **Date of the experiment**
- **Title of the experiment**
- **Purpose of the experiment:** summary information about experiment to be performed
- **Balanced chemical equations and reaction mechanisms**, if applicable. This will be necessary to correctly calculate reaction yield.
- **Hand written table of chemicals** that include physicochemical data for **all** chemicals used.

A table of the reactants, solvents, drying agents and products in the experiment must be included and each of these must be listed in its own row. There are 10 column headings: IUPAC name OR *common name,* structure, CAS number (Chemical Abstract Service number) molecular mass, melting point *(if applicable)*, boiling point *(if applicable)*, solubility (in water, *if applicable*), density, amounts to be used in the experiment, and the role. All chemicals used in the experiment must be listed and include correct units, spelling, amounts and roles (reagent/solvent/drying agent/product).

An example of the format for a table of chemicals is shown below:

IUPAC or common name	Structure	CAS #	Molecular mass (units)	Melting point (units)	Boiling point (units)	Solubility (in water)	Density (units)	Amounts to be used (units)	Role of the reagent

The compound's CAS number (Chemical Abstract Service number) is a unique identifier that unambiguously identifies chemical compound and is frequently used in database search. CAS # is very handy as some compounds can have multiple common names.

Also, unless otherwise instructed, the following items are also part of your pre-lab preparation:

Theoretical yield calculations

If applicable the following must be included and hand written: (1) a correctly balanced reaction equation, (2) a correct reaction mechanism, (3) a detailed and correct calculation of the number of moles of the reactants, (4) correct identification of the limiting reagent and (5) correct theoretical yield of product(s). All calculations, units and unit conversions must be clearly shown to gain full credit. The reaction mechanism(s) must include: curved arrow notation to account for electron flow, lone pairs of electrons, charges and correct molecular/ion structures. Reaction equations must be correctly balanced and show correct chemical formulae and reaction arrows. Solvents should not be included in the reaction equation, mechanism or any calculations.

Drawings of glassware/apparatus used

Relax, you will not be judged by the beauty of your artwork. However, your drawings must make sense and must be unambiguous. All items must be clearly labeled.

Hand written flowchart showing experimental procedures

Flowchart is a brief outline for carrying out each experimental step in your own words, and which must be hand written (Figure 16). A standard diagram flowchart format to map out the procedural steps should be utilized with rectangles encompassing each action or instruction point. The action/instruction points should be correctly spelled and include correct chemical formulae, quantities and units. You are expected to be able to perform your experiment only from the flowchart.

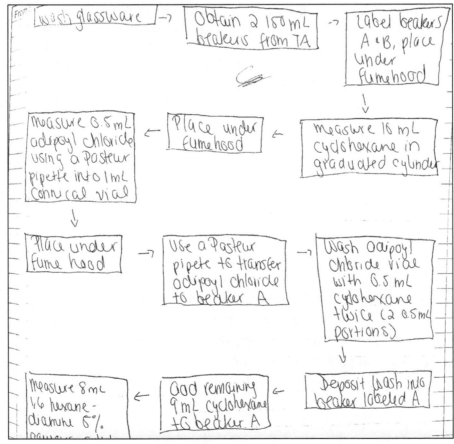

Figure 16. Sample flowchart.

At the beginning of each lab session your TA will sign-off on your pre-lab work. It is important that you take writing your pre-lab seriously as it will influence your overall performance in the lab while you perform your experiments!

Taking notes in the laboratory

In the laboratory, while you perform your experiments you are required to enter the following information into your notebook:

Detailed experimental procedures and observations

Procedures and observations must be hand written directly into lab notebook, in third person, and as the student performs the experiment. The procedures and observations cannot be pre-written or pasted-in. Correct formatting for this section: divide the page into two columns, with the left column labeled as "Procedures" and right column labeled as "Observations".

For the ***Procedures Column***: there must be an all-inclusive step by step write up of the experimental procedure as was carried out by the student. This can be in point form or sentence format, but must include detailed instructions that could be easily duplicated by a third party to carry out this procedure /experiment. All procedural step descriptions should be spelled correctly.

For the ***Observations Column***: each observation noted should correlate to the correct procedural step listed in the left hand column. An observation describes either what the student saw (e.g. color change, phase change, temperature change, relative distance traveled of compounds *versus* solvent from TLC separations etc.) or how much of a chemical the student measured/weighed out to use in any given step of the procedure or how much of the product was obtained as well as the product melting point (if applicable). Any chemical test(s) carried out must be included in this section with descriptive observations. The correct units must be recorded in this column.

Experimental results & spectral analysis

If applicable, the following information should record in your lab notebook:
   a. Actual yield(s) (re-recorded from the observations section).
   b. Melting point range(s) (re-recorded from the observations section).
   c. Your IR and NMR spectra fully assigned (stapled to the report to the back); key vibrations labeled (for IR) and peak resonances labeled (for NMR). Each spectrum must also have the molecular name and structure hand drawn (in pen) on the spectrum (Figure 17 & 18).

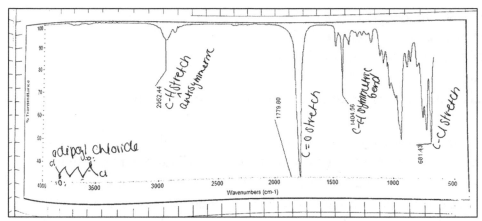

Figure 17. Sample IR spectrum with analyzed and labeled signals.

d. Table(s) identifying functional groups by their vibrations and the corresponding group frequencies from any collected IR spectra and tables with NMR signal assignments which include signal splitting/multiplicity information as well integration for ^{1}H NMR.

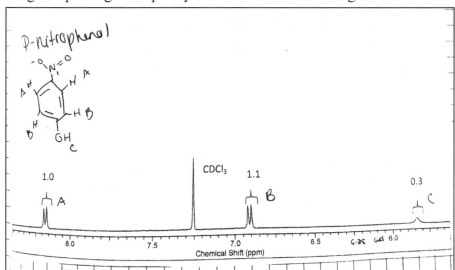

Figure 18. Sample 1H NMR spectrum showing peak labeling.

e. TLC plates must be labeled for the solvent front, elution spots and elution start line. You also have to draw the TLC plate image in the notebook as the plate is very fragile and prone to physical damage.

f. When applicable, the results of the chemical test(s) should be briefly re-summarized from the observations section and any applicable chemical equation included.

Any spectra acquired or provided, must be fully analyzed and stapled at the end of your typed laboratory report. Spectra analysis notes (compound's structure, labeled peaks) must be written on spectrum so that it is present on the copy page.

If applicable, also include the following:

    a. Re-evaluation of theoretical yield.

    b. Calculation of percentage (%) yield.

    c. Density calculations.

    d. R_f value calculations based on the distances recorded in the observations section.

Correct units must be used throughout this section and all unit conversions and calculations must be shown clearly and in detail to gain full credit. Key vibrations in the diagnostic region of IR spectra (above 1500 cm^{-1}) and which correspond to major functional groups present in a given molecule must be identified on each spectrum. In addition, key secondary IR vibrations of the unique functional groups, usually already assigned from the diagnostic region, must also be assigned in the fingerprint region (1500-500 cm^{-1}). All IR vibration labels on the spectra must clearly show the functional group and the nature of the vibration (e.g. stretching/bending).

All resonance signals must be assigned on the NMR spectra. These labels must correlate to either the correct proton or carbon atoms (for ^{1}H or ^{13}C NMR respectively) in the hand-drawn labeled molecular structure on each spectrum. For ^{1}H NMR spectra the integral ratios must be shown on the spectrum. The table(s) summarizing ^{1}H NMR spectra must clearly identify how many protons are represented by each resonance signal as well as the multiplicity of each signal.

Your signature

By signing your laboratory notebook, you certify that you've performed the experiment and you are exclusive author of your notebook's content.

At the end of the experiment you will complete the following section:

Experiment conclusions

This section should be completed by brief re-summarization in 2-3 sentences of the outcome from the experiment.

With your completed experiment and laboratory notes you are ready to write a laboratory report.

7. Laboratory reports

Writing style

Scientific writing must be precise and unambiguous to be effective. In this class through a series of written lab reports you will have a chance to practice your scientific writing. The format of laboratory reports used in this course is common for all (bio)chemical sciences and is used in most of scientific communication styles found in journals.

Every scientist has a personal writing style, but all good writings follow guidelines and conventions. In this class, we will follow the American Chemical Society (ACS) guide:

**The ACS Style Guide: Effective Communication of Scientific
Information, 3rd ed.**
Edited by Anne M. Coghill and Lorrin R. Garson
ISBN13: 9780841239999

Here is some information background provided by the publisher:
"The ACS Style Guide is the definitive source for all information needed to write, review, submit, and edit scholarly and scientific manuscripts. An established resource for the chemistry community, *The ACS Style Guide* is not just a resource for ACS authors, but is referenced by other publishers, even beyond chemistry, within their instructions to authors and is used as a resource in teaching students how to effectively communicate scientific information".
The ACS Style guide is available in PDF format at http://pubs.acs.org/isbn/9780841239999. Details on how to access this EBook are posted on course's website – Canvas. Please use this guide when writing your laboratory reports. Especially valuable/helpful for you will be chapters 4 and 9 through 18.

Report format

Your laboratory reports are required to be typed, printed out and together with your original pages from your laboratory notebook handed to your TA at the beginning of the class on the due date.
You may use **Arial**, Times New Roman or Calibri font with the size of 12 pts (not smaller). Line spacing must be 1.15 points. Margins must be kept normal (1 inch, all sides). If not specified otherwise a standard 5-page writing limit lab report cap (excluding peak tables and attached spectra) will apply.

Your laboratory report must contain the following sections:

Title page

The title page clearly identifies your laboratory report, title of the experiment and your section. This is the first page of your report. No other information can be present on this page.

Introduction

Summarizes the main features of the report (objectives); provides background information on the theoretical problem (as outlined is specific experiments) and the reason why it was investigated; discusses the significance of the experiment and introduces the method of approach to the problem. In this section, no data is present nor discussed.

Results

In this section you construct tables, charts, insert obtained (IR, NMR) spectra and/or figures that effectively present your results in a clear, organized and concise way. Your data tables, chemical drawings etc. must be included at the end of the report, just before attached spectra and notebook pages. This is required due to report page cap. Requirements for this section may vary from experiment to experiment and the details and expectations will be announced in the laboratory for each experiment. Your spectroscopic and yield data must be typed and present in your written report.

Discussion

Using the suitable verb tense helps to orient the reader as to the nature of the information.
This section can be written in first person (plural) form (e.g. we, ours). The use of simple past tense is appropriate for stating what was done, either by others or by you. For more info please see chapter 4 of ACS Style guide.
This section discusses exhaustively the underlying principles evidenced by the experiment. It also explains thoroughly to what extent the experimental results obtained assist in resolving or failing to resolve the initial problem. In this section, there must be no background/theory written. Your analyzed data must be explained in terms of chemical phenomena.
There is no value in just rewriting spectroscopic data using words – data tables serve for that. For example - peak 1 was observed at 1 ppm, peak 2 was observed ad 4 ppm... You are expected to explain what is the meaning of those signals. Using the above example you would like to say: peak 1 observed at 1 ppm as a singlet comes form a methyl group...because...(provide reference value).

Conclusion(s)

In this section, you summarize the main features of the report, the objectives, findings and conclusions. You briefly explain any possible sources of error relevant to your results.

References

You must use appropriate references when discussing your data or using reference values. The references must be listed at the end of your report.

When citing references in text you will be using one the ACS reference format. References and notes in the text should be indicated by superscript Arabic numerals that run consecutively through the paper and appear after any punctuation. Authors should ensure that all references are cited in the text and vice versa. Authors are expected to check the original source reference for accuracy.

Example: The synthesis of this compound was reported previously.[3]

Briefly, recommended ACS style reference format is as follows:
Author 1; Author 2; Author 3; etc. Title of the Article. *Journal Abbreviation* Year, *Volume*, Inclusive pagination
Example:

Zhiyuan Huang, Qingquan Lu, Yichang Liu, Dong Liu, Jian Zhang, and Aiwen Lei Regio- and Stereoselective Oxysulfonylation of Allenes *Organic Letters* **2016** *18*, 3940-3943

All other types of publications (including websites) must follow ACS style formatting.

8. Laboratory experiments

Laboratory experiments

The following laboratory experiments are performed during CHM2211L course:

The laboratory experiments may be modified at any time. Please pay close attention to announcements on Canvas and in the laboratory.

Identification of unknown compound by NMR spectroscopy

Purpose

This exercise illustrates how ^{1}H and ^{13}C NMR spectroscopy is used to elucidate the structure of organic compounds. Students will gain hands-on experience with running benchtop 42.5 MHz Spinsolve Carbon® NMR spectrometer (Magritek). The obtained ^{1}H, ^{13}C NMR spectra which will be supplemented with chemical formulae and DEPT-135 data experiments will give students chance to elucidate structure of unknown alcohol.

Number of laboratory sessions: 1

Pre-lab preparation

1. In your notebook <u>draw</u> a flowchart showing all procedures required for this experiment. Remember to include spectrometer preparation step.
2. For the basic introduction to NMR spectroscopy please read selected book chapters. Links are provided on Canvas. You can find them in "modules" section.
3. Please read detailed instructions on how to record and process NMR spectra. These can be found in chapter 4.
4. Watch mandatory video tutorial: NMR Spectra acquisition using Spinsolve. This video is available on Canvas under "Pages" section or is included in "modules" section. **You must watch it a number of times until you are comfortable with performing the data acquisition.**
5. Take the mandatory quiz before your lab session (announced on Canvas).

In the laboratory

At the beginning of the lab your TA will talk about analysis of NMR spectra and structure elucidation. Please pay close attention and take notes as this information will be necessary for you to complete this exercise. Next, each student will run their unknown alcohol sample. For this experiment, we will be using a neat alcohol sample – it means that no deuterated solvent will be present. Your TA will set up the spectrometer and insert the sample for you. Next, you will run Spinsolve software to obtain ^{1}H NMR spectrum, and later ^{13}C NMR spectrum.

To be proficient with this exercise you must watch posted video tutorials. Once you finish your runs you will be given a previously acquired DEPT-135 spectrum of your unknown alcohol. NMR structure elucidation is similar to puzzle solving. You have to take into account all of your peaks and other provided data (chemical formula). This process is shown on Figure 19, below.

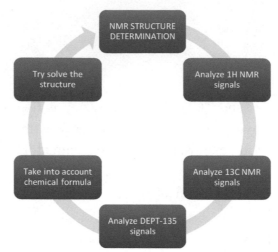

Figure 19 General method for NMR based structure elucidation used in this experiment.

While working on structure determination, in your laboratory notebook write down procedures and observations and create the NMR signals tables (see below) in your lab notebook (separate for ^{1}H, ^{13}C and DEPT-135 spectra).

For ^{1}H NMR spectrum:

Atom	Atom is part of a group	Peak Multiplicity	Peak observed (ppm)
A	CH$_2$	doublet	1.23
…			

For ^{13}C NMR spectrum:

Atom	Atom is part of a group	Peak observed (ppm)
1	CH$_2$	40.2
…		

For DEPT-135 spectrum:

Atom	Atom is part of a group	Peak observed (ppm)	Peak phase (+/-)
1	CH$_2$	40.2	-
…			

Try to draw your hypothetical structure and see if it makes sense (based on the data that you have).

Let's look at the spectra below and try to analyze them. Figure 20 shows sample spectrum that you will acquire/obtain in the lab.

Take a look at ^{1}H NMR spectrum first.

- Can you identify a signal that gives a clear integration for a known number of protons? Now work from left to right, assigning each signal, or groups of signals that you observe, to protons in your proposed structure. (If there is logic in starting at the left of the spectrum, it is that most molecules have some aromatic or heterocyclic core, to which, various alkyl functions are attached. If there is a problem with the core, then you will at least discover it promptly and be able to relate it to the alkyl components of the molecule.)

- Cross-examine each and every signal in your spectrum to check that they conform to the expected values for the three crucial NMR parameters: (1) chemical shift, (2) coupling pattern and (3) integration.

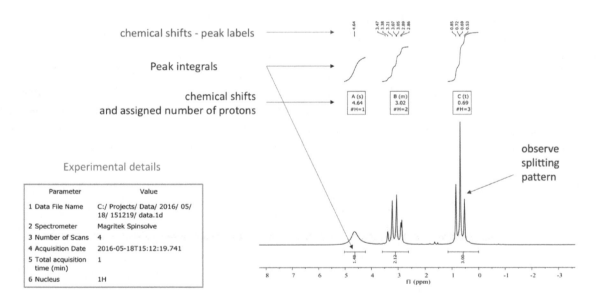

Figure 20. Example of 1H NMR spectrum obtained in the laboratory. The assigned number of protons comes from automatic computer assignment and may not be correct.

Look at Figure 21. A simple algorithm for solving ^{1}H NMR spectra is provided.

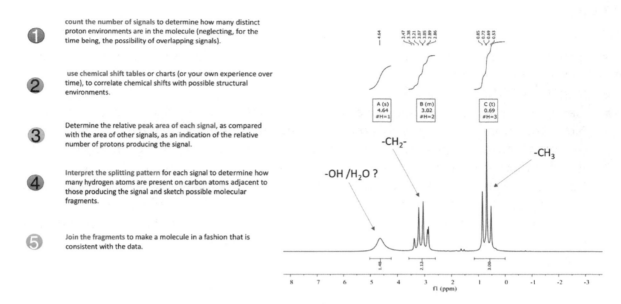

Figure 21. Simple algorithm used for structure elucidation using NMR.

^{13}C NMR spectrum will give you information on carbon chemical environments present. These are decoupled spectra so no splitting information is present. Quaternary carbon's frequently give small peaks. Acquisition conditions are not optimized for integration.

A DEPT-135 spectrum will help you distinguish CH_3, CH, CH_2 carbons. DEPT-135 stands for Distortionless Enhancement of Polarization Transfer using a 135 degree decoupler pulse. This pulse sequence produces a carbon spectrum with methyl (CH_3) and methyne (CH) carbons are up. Methene (CH_2) carbons are down. Quaternary carbon atoms are not visible in this kind of spectrum. During spectra analysis please consider possible symmetry in the molecule!

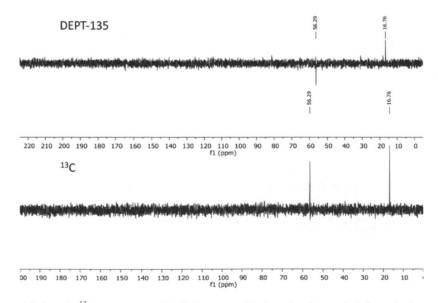

Figure 22. Sample ^{13}C and DEPT-135 NMR spectra. Look at the chemical shifts on both spectra.

Chemical formula – the missing piece of information.

You are given a chemical formula of your unknown alcohol sample. Together with integrated ^{1}H NMR signals and ^{13}C analysis you will be able to determine the structure of your alcohol. This lab exercise is like chemical Sudoku game!

Please ask your TA for the chemical formula of your unknown sample.

Predicting NMR spectra

Sometimes analysis of NMR spectra can be difficult. To facilitate this process, one can use special software capable of ^{1}H and ^{13}C spectra predictions. You can do that using Chemdoodle, for example.
However, a better way is to use NMR prediction server available at: http://www.nmrdb.org. Please remember to use proper citation when using this tool.[11]

The use of this online tool is pretty straightforward: Just draw your molecule and click **Calculate spectrum**. Please see example below:

Step 1: Draw chemical structure of your molecule
Step 2: Click Calculate spectrum. Your spectrum will be generated.
You can interact with the spectrum (zoom, scroll…) by moving cursor over peaks or particular atoms in the formula window. Your corresponding peaks will be highlighted.

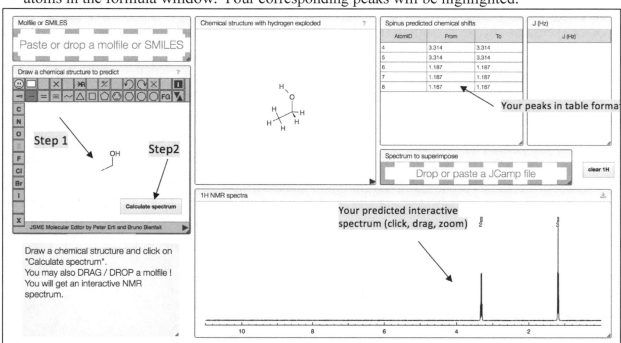

Figure 23. Screenshot from the nmrdb.org website.

You are required to predict the ^{1}H and ^{13}C NMR spectra of your hypothesized alcohol and compare them with your experimental data.

What is expected on the report

All standard lab report sections apply. Please see chapter 7 for details. More specifically, the following items are also required:

Introduction

Provide background information on the theoretical problem – how to solve structures of organic molecules? How signal interpretation help identify structure, functional groups *etc.*; observed peaks vs. electronic structure; Theory of NMR – (the physics of how the signal is being generated, Fourier transformation, etc.) is not required. However, explanation of factors influencing chemical shifts are expected.

Results and discussion

Results:
- drawn structure of your alcohol (must be drawn on the spectrum)
- labels of all proton signals (letters…A…Z) and carbon signals (numbers…1…n)
- tabular comparison of your observed <u>and</u> calculated spectrum peaks (for both ^{1}H and ^{13}C spectra)

Discussion:
- Discussion of your signals (proton, carbon) and relationship between observed and calculated peaks and provided chemical formula (similarities/differences, overlaps…etc). Do not simply mention them – <u>discuss your reasoning in structure elucidation</u>. Explain the molecular structure vs. signal relationship. Note that predicted spectrum may slightly vary. Why? Explain.
  Especially the –O**H** peak signal may not be seen/predicted correctly. Why? Explain.
  Add these points to your discussion as well. Remember: the discussion section always compares one's findings with existing literature!
  Note: Predicted NMR spectra/signals are not your literature values! Reported literature values are always experimentally determined. You can cite chemical shift data tables.

Conclusion(s)

Briefly explain any possible sources of error relevant to your results. Have you successfully determined the structure? Why/why not?

References

Please cite any references in ACS format. Remember to cite every source that helped you. Citation of other college/common websites are forbidden as they are not the valid source of information.

DO NOT cite this manual, other courses' websites, only original works! Only primary citation sources such as journals and books will give you a full credit.

Report submission

Your complete lab report must include
1. Hard copy of your lab report & online submission.
2. Original pages from your lab notebook. Pages cannot be loose. You must staple/bind them before submission.
3. Stapled, and labeled original NMR spectra that you worked on in the lab.

Please pay attention to report deadlines. See Canvas for details.

Literature

(1)   Banfi, D.; Patiny, L. Nmrdb.org: Resurecting and Processing NMR Spectra Online. *Chimia (Aarau).* **2008**, *64* (2), 280–281.

Identification of unknown compound by IR spectroscopy and melting point analysis

Purpose

Identification of organic compounds is one of the essential skills needed in an organic chemistry laboratory. The purpose of this introductory experiment is to identify the unknown organic compound based on infrared spectroscopy (IR) and melting point (m.p.) analyses. Through this hands-on guided laboratory experience students learn how to analyze the structure of an unknown organic compound: how to determine the presence of various functional groups using IR spectroscopy, how to record melting point values and how to deduct the structure using additional information from ^{13}C NMR spectroscopy data.

Number of laboratory sessions: 2

Pre-lab preparation

1. For the basic introduction to IR spectroscopy please read selected book chapters. Links are provided on Canvas. You can find them in the "modules" section.
2. Please read detailed instructions on how to record IR spectrum and perform m.p. analysis (chapter 4).
3. Please watch mandatory video tutorial on recording IR spectra and melting point determination (posted on Canvas). *Watching tutorial means that you feel comfortable with the presented technique and are able to repeat the experiment without looking at the video or your notes.*
4. Take online quiz (see Canvas) for that experiment that relates to tutorial video and procedures in the lab. Due dates are posted on Canvas.
5. In your notebook draw a flowchart showing all procedures required for this experiment.

In the laboratory

The identification of your unknown compound using different methods from this experiment is an interactive process, depicted on Figure 24.

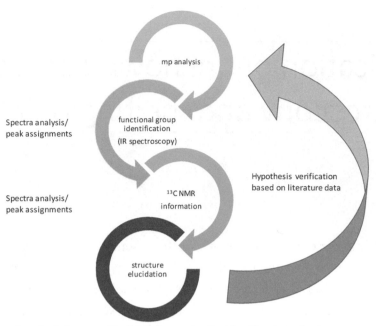

Figure 24. General methodology used in this lab exercise for identification of unknown compound.

At the beginning of the **first laboratory session** your TA will talk about analysis of IR spectra and functional group identification. Please pay close attention and take notes as this information will be necessary for you to complete this laboratory session. Next, each student will obtain the sample of unknown organic compound (~ 50 mg). You will be instructed on how to use m.p. apparatus and IR spectrometer (please read chapter 4, where detailed instructions are written). Under the guidance and supervision of your TA your you must:

1. Perform melting point analysis for unknown compound. Your melting points should be within a 5 °C range (melting starts → fully melted). For example, if your observed melting point range was 100-102 °C you are correct. If your recorded range was 100-107 °C you will have to repeat the measurement.

2. Record the IR spectrum of your unknown sample, print it out and analyze it.

All your data must be recorded (inserted) directly into your research notebook. Spectra must be fully analyzed and labeled. Your IR data must be presented in a table format and must include the proper peak description for each identified functional group/key vibrations:

Sample IR data table

functional group	Molecular motion	Observed wavenumber [cm^{-1}]	Literature value (range) [cm^{-1}]	Peak intensity	Peak shape
Carboxylic acid	**C=O stretch** (stretch, bend…symmetric, antisymmetric)			**very strong,** (strong, medium, weak-to-medium, weak…)	**broad** (narrow, sharp…)

To identify functional groups present in your unknown sample, you will use the IR absorption bands table found in the Appendix, at the end of this book. Names and structures of various functional groups are also found in the Appendix.

The key vibrations (identified peaks) and melting point must be *discussed* in the "Results and Discussion" section of your laboratory report.

In the **second laboratory session** you will be given a ^{13}C NMR spectrum of your unknown compound which you will have to analyze and attach to your lab report. Similar to IR data, your NMR spectrum peaks must be reported in a table form (see previous experiment).

You must draw a structural formula on the spectrum label all carbon atoms with numbers 1...n and assign all corresponding signals on your ^{13}C NMR spectrum (see Figure 25)

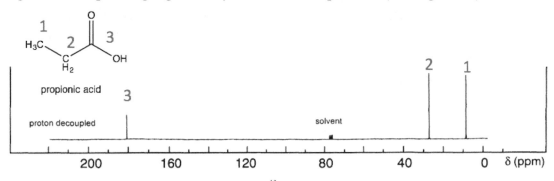

Figure 25. Proper ^{13}C NMR peak labeling.

Taking into consideration all of your obtained data (m.p., IR, ^{13}C NMR) draw your conclusions and predict/identify your unknown compound (See figure 24). Your guesses must be supported with reported (and properly cited) literature values!

What is expected on the report

All standard lab report sections apply. Please see chapter 7 for details. More specifically, the following items are also required:

Introduction

What is the idea behind this laboratory exercise? Provide background (concise) information on the theoretical problem – how to solve structures or characterize organic molecules using demonstrated techniques? Can instrumental techniques used in this experiment help also with compound's purity determination? If so, how?

Results and discussion

Results:

- Report m.p. of your compound.
- Draw structure of your compound on your IR and NMR spectra.
- Report your IR data in a table format (typed).
- Labels of all carbon signals *1…n* on ^{13}C NMR spectrum and report NMR data in a table format (see previous NMR experiment)

Discussion:

- Discussion of your signals (NMR and IR) and relationship between observed and literature values for your identified peaks (similarities/differences, overlaps…etc). Do not simply mentioned them – discuss your reasoning (and evidence) in structure elucidation.

  However, once you have identified your compound, for even better comparison with literature values you may want to look up various chemical databases to further confirm your findings (make sure to cite them).

Conclusion(s)

Have you successfully determined the structure? Why/why not? What was the evidence?

References

Please cite any references in ACS format. Remember to cite every source that helped you. Citation of other college/common websites are forbidden as they are not the valid source of information. DO NOT cite this manual, other courses' websites, only original works! Only primary citation sources such as journals and books will give you a full credit.

Report submission

Your complete lab report must include
1. Hard copy of your lab report & online submission.
2. Original pages from your lab notebook. Pages cannot be loose. You must staple/bind them before submission.
3. Attach original IR/NMR spectra and original pages from your lab notebook to a hard copy report.

Please pay attention to report deadlines. See Canvas for details.

Synthesis of Nylon-6,6

Purpose

In this experiment students will explore polymerization reaction to obtain nylon-6,6 (polyamide). Nylon-6,6 is obtained through condensation reaction between adipoyl chloride and 1,6-hexanediamine monomers employing an interfacial polymerization technique. The obtained polymer will be further characterized using IR spectroscopy.

Number of laboratory sessions: 1

Background information

Nylon-6,6 is a polyamide and one of the first non-natural polymers that was discovered. The first successful synthesis of nylon-6 was reported by S. Gabriel in 1899.[1] The polymer was obtained by heating ε-aminocaproic acid. In 1934 W.H. Carothers invented nylon-6,6 and DuPont pioneered its commercial production in 1941. The nomenclature used for nylon polymers was created during the synthesis of the first simple aliphatic nylons and uses numbers to describe the number of carbons between acid and amine functions (Figure 26).

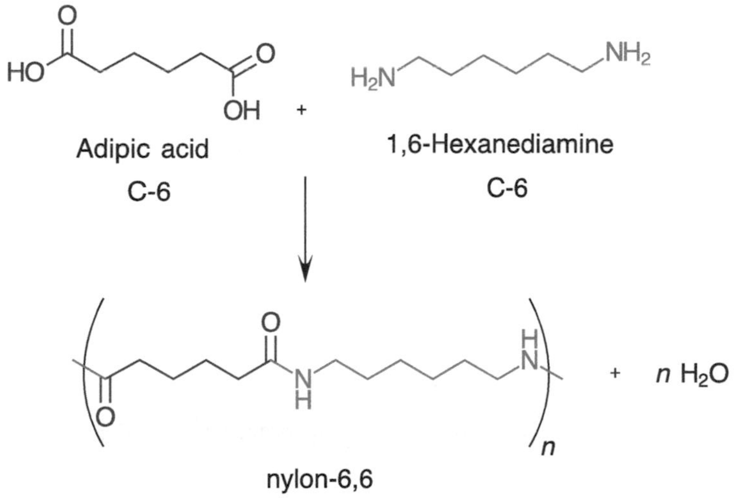

Figure 26. Nylon synthesis and naming convention.

Since its commercial introduction, nylon-type polymers became important for our society and are used for a variety of purposes such as ropes, cords, belts, clothes and many more.[2]

Nylon-6,6 can be synthesized by the reaction of two bifunctional monomers: adipic acid and 1,6-hexanediamine or adipoyl chloride and 1,6-hexanediamine. The first method is used in the industry and requires high temperature (250-275 °C) and long reaction times. In our laboratory we will be using the second method. With some experimental care, under basic conditions, the reaction between adipoyl chloride dissolved in water immiscible solvent (hexanes) and the aqueous solution of the diamine can be carried out at room temperature and can be accomplished in minutes (Figure 27).[3]

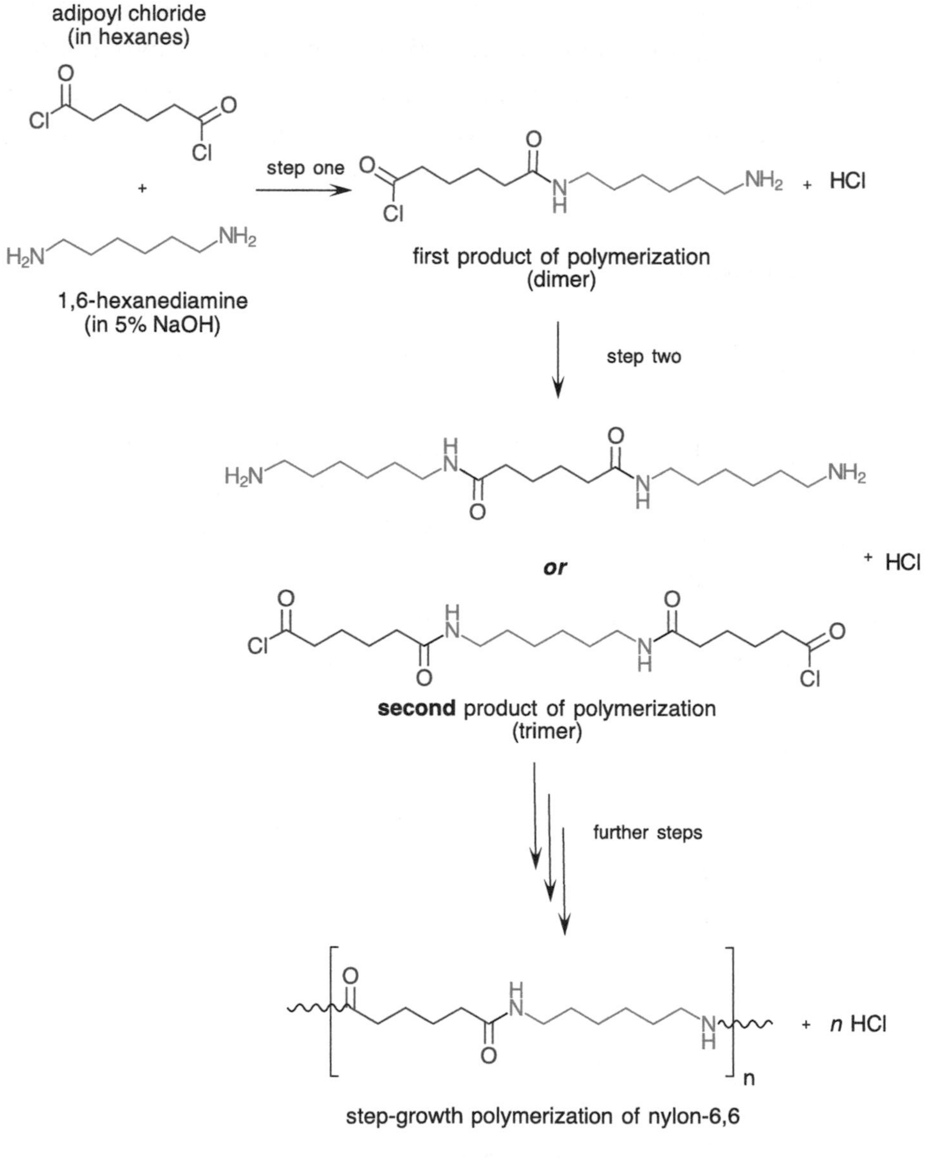

Figure 27. Nylon-6,6 synthesis to be performed in this laboratory. Step-growth polymerization reaction is shown.

The reaction of adipoyl chloride with 1,6-hexanediamine to form nylon-6,6 is classified as a "step-growth" polymerization reaction, where polymers once formed may combine with one another or with monomers to increase the polymer chain length. Do not confuse it with "chain-growth" polymerization reaction where the growing polymer chain is limited to reaction with monomers to increase polymer chain length.

The reaction between adipoyl chloride and 1,6-hexanediamine is also a condensation reaction since small molecule (HCl, in this case) is formed each time a monomer (of polymer fragment) adds to the growing polymer chain.

The interfacial polymerization reaction refers to the formation of a thin film of the nylon-6,6 polymer at the interface of the two phases which contain the two monomers. The adipoyl chloride must be dissolved in a water immiscible solvent due to its instability in water. To facilitate the reaction, the 1,6-hexanediamine aqueous phase must contain a strong base such as NaOH. The polymerization reaction continues and the growing nylon fiber can be drawn slowly from the interface using a copper wire or other device. In seconds, the polymer can grow to average molecular weights around 5,000 – 20,000 Daltons.

Pre-lab preparation

In your lab notebook, prepare the following (see lab notebook guide for details):
1. Draw a flowchart showing all procedures required for this experiment. Prepare it so that it can be used as a sole source of your experimental procedures.
2. Detailed, hand-written mechanism of initial steps of polymerization reaction between adipoyl chloride and 1,6-hexanediamine (up to trimer formation). Must include arrows, electron flow and lone pairs.
3. Hand written table of chemicals that includes physicochemical data for **all** chemicals used (see chapter 6).
4. Theoretical yield calculations. Explain in short paragraph (in your lab notebook) why for this experiment it is not possible to calculate the theoretical yield.
5. Drawings of all the glassware and instrumentation used for the experiment. Glassware must be properly named.
6. Explain in short paragraph (in lab notebook) the role of 25% NaOH solution used in the reaction.

In the laboratory

The essential reactants for nylon-6,6 synthesis are provided in Table 1.

Table 1.

Reactants used					
Compound	MW	amount used	mmol	bp (°C)	d (g/mL)
Adipoyl chloride	183.05	0.4 mL	3.4		1.26
5% aqueous solution of 1,6-hexanediamine	116.2	8 mL		42	
cyclohexane	84.16	8 mL		80.7	0.78
25% aqueous solution of NaOH	40	8 droplets			

Experimental procedure: polymerization

For this experiment, you will use two 150 mL (or similar) beakers. Please label them A and B respectively and place them in your work space in the fume hood. Next, collect 10 mL of cyclohexane in a graduated cylinder and transfer it to a beaker labeled "A". Afterwards, obtain the 0.4 mL of adipoyl chloride from your TA. Transfer the adipoyl chloride to the 150 mL beaker (labeled "A"). Swirl the beaker gently so that all the adipoyl chloride is dissolved.

Next, collect 8 mL of 1,6-hexanediamine 5% aqueous solution in a graduated cylinder and take it to your work space in the fume hood. Add the 1,6-hexanediamine to empty 150 mL beaker (labeled "B"). Next, add 8 drops of 25% NaOH solution NaOH solution SLOWLY to 1,6-hexanediamine in beaker "B" and swirl the beaker gently in order to mix it.

Now, taking care to run the solution down the side of the beaker wall, transfer organic solution from beaker "A" into beaker "B" (A → B). Please consult with your TA as to the proper addition technique in this step to ensure that you obtain nylon-6,6 polymer. Right after adding the two solutions together start pulling your nylon.

Using a straw ("umbrella"), hook the nylon film forming at the interface of the two phases and very slowly lift upwards without fully removing the film from the solution. Continue pulling the nylon as more of it forms. Wind it on a test tube (see Figure 28). A slow, steady pull will result in a longer nylon polymer. Your nylon must be shown to your TA for inspection. Rinse your polymer with water, pat it dry (using a paper towel) and weigh it. Record the mass of your polymer in your lab notebook. To store your polymer, place it on a paper towel in your drawer. It will be used in the future experiment.

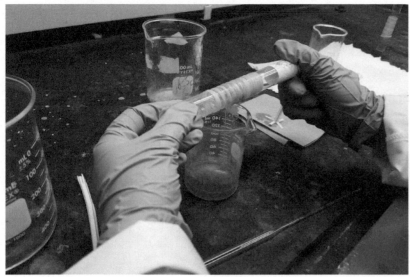

Figure 28. Pulling nylon-6,6 (left) using straw "umbrella" (right).

Procedure: product characterization

Record the IR spectrum of your synthesized polymer and analyze it. Record all information in your lab notebook. Are the IR bands that you found in the spectrum of the polymer consistent with your expectations for this polyamide? Print out the IR spectra of the two monomers (spectra are posted on Canvas) analyze it and attached it to your lab report.

What is expected on the report

All standard lab report sections apply. Please see chapter 7 for details. More specifically, the following items are also required:

Introduction

In a brief paragraph (max half page long) explain what are the different types of polymerization reactions and give specific examples of polymers (products) of those reactions.

Results and discussion

Results:
- IR data analysis (all spectra).
- Provide a brief information on your results (spectra, data tables, figures, etc.) and where they can be found (include them after the main text so that the page limit for text is not affected).

- Report the physicochemical properties of your synthesized nylon-6,6 (mass, physical appearance)

Discussion:

- Discuss your IR spectra analysis (report your IR data in a usual table format), draw structure of your compound on all your spectra. Discuss similarities/differences between product and reagents. Attach the original spectra at the end of your report.
- Discuss the role of interchain molecular interactions observed between the single chains of nylon molecules that stabilize fiber formation (any analogy to the biological systems?). Depict using Chemdoodle made drawing.

Conclusion(s)

Summarize the main features of the report, the objectives, findings and conclusions. Briefly explain any possible sources of error relevant to your results. Have you successfully performed the experiment? Why/why not? Was your synthesis/purification/analysis successful (yield…)?

References

Please cite any references in ACS format. Remember to cite every source that helped you. Citation of other college/common websites are forbidden as they are not the valid source of information. DO NOT cite this manual, other courses' websites, only original works! Only primary citation sources such as journals and books will give you a full credit.

Report submission

Your complete lab report must include
1. Hard copy of your lab report & online submission.
2. Original pages from your lab notebook. Pages cannot be loose. You must staple/bind them before submission.
3. Attach original IR/NMR spectra and original pages from your lab notebook to a hard copy report.

Please pay attention to report deadlines. See Canvas for details.

References

(1) Gabriel, S.; Maass, T. A. Ueber ε-Amidocapronsäure. *Berichte der Dtsch. Chem. Gesellschaft* **1899**, *32* (1), 1266–1272.
(2) Heckert, W. W. Synthetic Fibers. *J. Chem. Educ.* **1953**, *30* (4), 166.
(3) Morgan, P. W.; Kwolek, S. L. The Nylon Rope Trick: Demonstration of Condensation Polymerization. *J. Chem. Educ.* **1959**, *36* (4), 182.

Synthesis and characterization of acetanilide and other analgesics

Purpose

In this experiment, you will synthesize acetanilide from aniline and acetic anhydride. The acetanilide will then be purified by recrystallization, characterized by m.p., ^{1}H NMR and thin layer chromatography (TLC). Thin layer chromatography will be then used to identify acetanilide in a mixture of other analgesics. This is your first complete organic chemistry experiment familiarizing you with the whole experimental cycle: organic synthesis, purification and compound characterization/identification.

Number of laboratory sessions: 3

Background information

Acetanilide (N-phenylacetamide) is an obsolete analgesic and antipyretic agent, also known as antifebrin. It was abandoned long ago due to its excessive toxicity and low activity. The acetanilide can be synthesized in a number of ways. In this laboratory you will use aniline and acetic acid anhydride as key reagents (Figure 29).

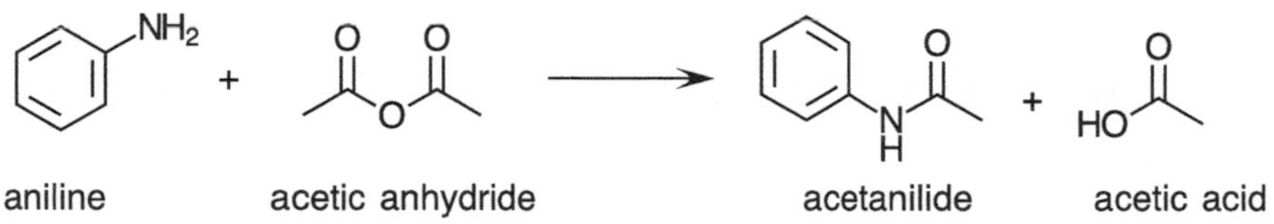

aniline   acetic anhydride   acetanilide   acetic acid

Figure 29. The overall reaction scheme for acetanilide synthesis.

The acetanilide is soluble in hot water (~5.5 g/100 mL) and scarcely soluble in cold (~0.5 g/100 mL). We will use this property to purify it by recrystallization.

Recrystallization is a common purification technique used in an organic chemistry laboratory. The desired, to be purified product should be as soluble as possible in hot solvent and as insoluble as possible in cold solvent. The selection of solvent is, therefore, critical to successful recrystallization. Recrystallization is a widely-used technique to purify a solid mixture. The desired product is isolated from its impurities by differences in solubility at various temperatures.

Soluble impurities remain in the cold solvent after recrystallization. In case of acetanilide, water will be used.

In this experiment, you will be introduced to several new laboratory techniques:
1. Dispensing of reagents using micropipettes
2. Using analytical balance
3. Recrystallization
4. Hirsch funnel filtration
5. Thin layer chromatography.

Description of essential lab techniques can be found in chapter 5. It is extremely important that you ***study*** the following laboratory instructions carefully and watch accompanying video tutorials (posted on Canvas) to be fully prepared for this laboratory session.

Pre-lab preparation

In your lab notebook, prepare the following (see lab notebook guide for details):
1. Draw a flowchart showing all procedures required for this experiment. Prepare it so that it can be used as a sole source of your experimental procedures.
2. Detailed, hand-written mechanism of acetanilide synthesis using aniline and acetic anhydride. Must include arrows, electron flow and lone pairs.
3. Hand written table of chemicals that include physicochemical data for **all** chemicals used (see chapter 6).
4. Theoretical yield calculations.
5. Drawings of all the glassware and instrumentation used for the experiment. Glassware must be properly named.
6. Calculate (in your lab notebook) the volume of liquid reagents used in the experiment (from Table 1)
7. Explain in short paragraph (in lab notebook) the role of 25% NaOH solution used in the reaction.

In the laboratory

The essential reactants for acetanilide synthesis are provided in Table 1.

Table 1.

Reactants used					
Compound	**MW**	**amount used**	**mmol**	**bp (°C)**	**d (g/mL)**
Acetic anhydride	102.09	240 mg		139.8	1.08
aniline	93.13	186 mg	2	184.1	1.02
water	18.02	2 mL		100	1

Experimental procedure: synthesis & recrystallization

To a 4 mL conical vial add 186 mg of aniline and a magnetic spin vane. Next, add 2 mL of water and stir it on a magnetic stirrer (DO NOT HEAT IT). After that, add 240 mg of acetic anhydride and keep stirring. At some point, solid should form. Note any changes that occur to the reaction mixture and the times at which they occurred. After 20 minutes, cool the reaction mixture in an ice bath to complete crystallization. Isolate the product by vacuum filtration using Hirsch funnel, wash it with <u>ice-cold</u> water (using Pasteur pipette), and allow it to dry on the funnel by pulling air through the solids for 5 minutes. Weigh your product and report the obtained yield. Next, prepare water bath. To a 100 mL beaker add 20 mL of water and heat it on the hot plate until boiling. Transfer your product into new conical vial for better recovery). Using a <u>minimal</u> amount of hot water (from water bath, added drop after drop) dissolve your acetanilide. You may want to keep your tube in a water bath while dissolving the product. After you obtain a clear solution remove your tube from the bath and let it cool down to room temperature. Once reached, place your tube into ice bath to further cool it down. Keep it on ice for 5 minutes and then filter it off using Hirsh funnel. Dry your product in the oven (TAs will set the oven temperature) and keep it for 10 min in there. Determine the recrystallization yield (percent recovery) and record it in your lab notebook.

Experimental procedure: product characterization

Perform TLC analysis of your recrystallized product. Compare it with commercial pure acetanilide and aniline as potential impurity (the solution of these samples will be provided to you). As a developing solvent system use 20% ethyl acetate in hexanes. How results compare with ^{1}H NMR spectrum?
Next, take 50 mg of your acetanilide and place it into 1.5 mL microcentrifuge tube. Hand your TA the weighted sample. It will be dissolved it in 400 µL of deuterated chloroform (dispensed by the TA) and record ^{1}H NMR spectrum. Use white NMR tube holder while inserting the NMR sample into spectrometer. Your TA will insert the NMR tube into the spectrometer. Acquire the spectrum, process it and print it out. Your TA will sign off on the spectrum. Compare your product's ^{1}H NMR spectrum with starting materials (spectra posted on Canvas).

Record the m.p. of your product. The m.p. apparatus will be set up by TA to cover the range of 80 - 150 °C.

Comparison of acetanilide with other analgesics

Your task is to identify acetanilide in the mixture of common over-the-counter painkillers using TLC technique. To be compared analgesics are: aspirin, acetaminophen, ibuprofen and caffeine. At first, you will run one TLC plate (3 plates per class) to obtain Rf values of these compounds. Complete the table below using data from 3 plates (average the results).

	Aspirin	Acetaminophen	Ibuprofen	Caffeine
Rf value				

Your developing solution is composed of 1% of acetic acid in ethyl acetate.

Next, you will be issued with TLC plate and you must complete the following:
1. Obtain the unknown sample that have been assigned to you.
2. Perform TLC analysis. Spot unknown sample and reference acetanilide sample (provided) only once/twice as it is very concentrated. Verify under UV light the presence/intensity of your spots before proceeding with TLC separation.
3. Identify acetanilide and other components of your unknown mixture using your TLC knowledge and reference R_f value from table above. Record all R_f values.

What is expected on the report

All standard lab report sections apply. Please see chapter 7 for details. More specifically, the following items are also required:

Introduction

Provide background information on the theoretical problems:
- How can one synthesize acetanilide? Why this synthetic route was performed?
- Why recrystallization was used as preferred purification method for acetanilide.
- What is the advantage of TLC as analytical technique and why it was used/helped in the characterization/identification of the compounds.
- What are the active ingredients used in over-the-counter analgesics? Provide chemical names and structural formulas for at least 4 of them (must be Chemdoodle drawn).

Results and discussion

Please to remember to reference all your spectra/images/tables in the text. Do not forget to make figure captions.

Results:

- Report the theoretical, obtained and recovery (recrystallization) yields. Show your calculations in your notebook.
- Report NMR spectra analysis of your product and starting materials (report your data in a usual table format having complete peak analysis), draw structure of your compound on all of your spectra. Discuss similarities/differences between product and reagents. <u>Attach the original spectra at the end of your report</u>.
- Provide m.p. analysis and literature value comparison. Cite your literature source.
- Report TLC analysis of aniline, commercial acetanilide and your recrystallized product. Report R_f values and discuss the results.
- Report TLC analysis of mixtures of analgesics. Were you able to identify all compounds? Why/Why not? Report all R_f values as well. Discuss results and analysis.
- Using ChemDoodle software (exclusively) draw the image of your TLC plate of your unknown analgesics mixture. Discuss the results. Insert your Chemdoodle drawn TLC image into your results section (MS Word).

Discussion:

- Discuss all your data (yields, synthetic problems, NMR and TLC analysis), by comparing it with literature values (not predictions!). Comment on the time when the acetanilide was formed and the physical appearance of crystals.

Conclusion(s)

Summarize the main features of the report, the objectives, findings and conclusions. You briefly explain any possible sources of error relevant to your results. Have you successfully performed the experiment? Why/why not? Was your synthesis/purification/analysis successful (yield…)?

References

Please cite any references in ACS format. Remember to cite every source that helped you. Citation of other college/common websites are forbidden as they are not the valid source of information. DO NOT cite this manual, other courses' websites, only original works! Only primary citation sources such as journals and books will give you a full credit.

Report submission

Your complete lab report must include
1. Hard copy of your lab report & online submission.

2. Original pages from your lab notebook. Pages cannot be loose. You must staple/bind them before submission.
3. Attach original IR/NMR spectra and original pages from your lab notebook to a hard copy report.

Please pay attention to report deadlines. See Canvas for details.

Fischer esterification of an unknown alcohol

Purpose

In this experiment, you will carry out Fischer esterification using acetic acid and an unknown alcohol to yield an unknown ester (acetate). Students will then isolate the acetate by distillation and characterize their unknown ester using IR and NMR spectroscopy to identify the chemical formulae names of both ester product and the starting unknown alcohol.

Number of laboratory sessions: 3

Background information

Esters and ester group bearing molecules represent a very important class of compounds widely distributed in nature. They play a significant role in biochemistry and are extensively used in commercial products from artificial sweeteners, polymers to surfactants and fragrances.
Esters are generally synthesized by one of four fundamental routes:
-   esterification of carboxylic acid with an alcohol in the presence of an acid catalyst
-   alcoholysis of acid chlorides, anhydrides or nitriles
-   reaction of carboxylate salt with an alkyl halide or sulfate
-   transesterification reaction.

The first of these synthetic methods is called Fischer esterification after Emil Fischer who first described this reaction in 1895.[1] Commonly used catalysts for a Fischer esterification include sulfuric acid, *p*-toluenesulfonic acid, and other Lewis acids. In this experiment, we will be using concentrated H_2SO_4 (Figure 30).

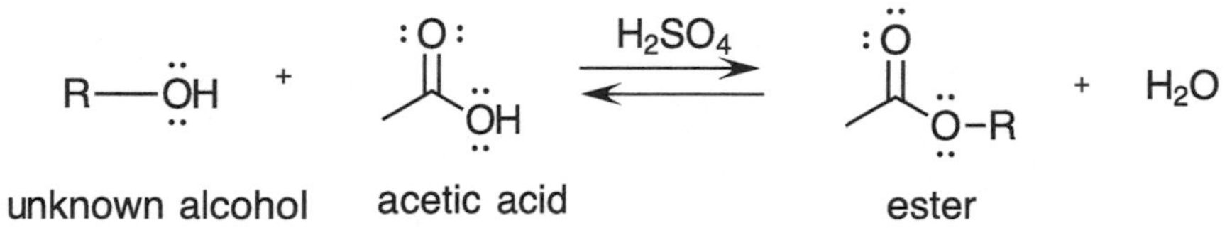

Figure 30. Fischer esterification reaction using acetic acid and unknown alcohol.

Fischer esterification is an equilibrium reaction and it is reversible. The Fischer esterification proceeds by nucleophilic attack of the alcohol on the protonated carbonyl group of the carboxylic acid to form a tetrahedral intermediate. Collapse of the tetrahedral intermediate regenerates the carbonyl group and results in ester and water formation. The rate of the reaction will be determined by the ease with which the nucleophile (alcohol or water) approaches the carbonyl group. Steric and electronic factors have been shown to have large effects on the rate of esterification. An increase in the number of bulky substituents in the α or β positions of the carbonyl containing compound decreases the rate (steric effect). Electron withdrawing groups near the carbonyl group tend to increase the reaction rate by increasing the electrophilicity (partial positive charge) of the carbonyl carbon atom (electronic effect). Conversely, electron-donating groups act to hinder the rate of esterification.

In the Fischer esterification with primary alcohols, the products are only slightly favored by the equilibrium and, therefore, to obtain substantial yields of the ester, the equilibrium must be shifted towards product formation. This goal can be accomplished in a number of ways. For example, an excess of the starting alcohol or carboxylic acid can be used to shift the position of equilibrium toward the ester formation. Another approach is to remove one or both products (ester, water) as they are formed during the reaction.

The preparation of the unknown ester in this laboratory experiment also depends on two of the strategies:
-   reaction is performed with the carboxylic acid excess, and
water formed as a product is removed by a drying reagent (calcium chloride).

Pre-lab preparation

In your lab notebook, prepare the following (see lab notebook guide for details):
1. Draw a flowchart showing all procedures required for this experiment. Prepare it so that it can be used as a sole source of your experimental procedures.
2. Detailed, hand-written reaction mechanism for Fischer esterification of primary alcohol (R-OH) with acetic acid using sulfuric acid as a catalyst. Must include arrows, electron flow and lone pairs.
3. Hand written table of chemicals that include physicochemical data for **all** chemicals used (see chapter 6).
4. Theoretical yield calculations. Is it possible to calculate the theoretical yield?
5. Drawings of all the glassware and instrumentation used for the experiment. Glassware must be properly named.

In the laboratory

In the first lab session you will be issued with your unknown alcohol sample. Make sure that you write down the unknown sample number in your notebook (under Procedures and Observations). In the second lab session you will isolate/purify your ester by simple distillation technique. During this session you will be issued with the IR and ^{13}C NMR spectra for your expected unknown ester which you will have to analyze in the lab during that session.

In the third lab session you will analyze ^{1}H NMR spectrum of your product.

The essential reactants for esterification reaction are provided in Table 1.

Table 1.

Reactants used					
Compound	MW	amount used	mmol	bp (°C)	d (g/mL)
Unknown alcohol		1 mL			
Acetic acid	60.1	1.5 mL	26.2	118	1.05
Sulfuric acid, conc.		4 drops			

Experimental procedure: setting up the reaction

Prepare (assemble) your glassware setup (Figure 31A): 5 mL conical vial containing a magnetic spin vane, reflux condenser and calcium chloride drying tube. Transfer it to the fume hood for reactant dispensing. Remove calcium drying tube from the setup and dispense 1 mL of unknown alcohol, 1.5 mL of glacial acetic acid and 4 drops of concentrated sulfuric acid through reflux condenser (from the top) using long Pasteur pipette. Cap the reflux condenser with calcium chloride drying tube immediately after addition of each reagent.

NOTE: Dispense the reagents under the hood using pipettes. Remember that acetic and sulfuric acids are corrosive.

After addition of all reactants heat and stir the reaction mixture using a hot plate. Your reaction mixture must be boiling (this corresponds to a temperature of ~130°C. Continue refluxing for 1 hour. Monitor the temperature using provided thermometer. Do not leave your reaction unattended. After 1 hour cool the resulting mixture to room temperature and remove spin vane with magnetic wand. At this point ask your TA if a further addition of ~0.5 mL diethyl ether is required to increase the volume of the organic phase in your reaction mixture before you proceed with the product isolation

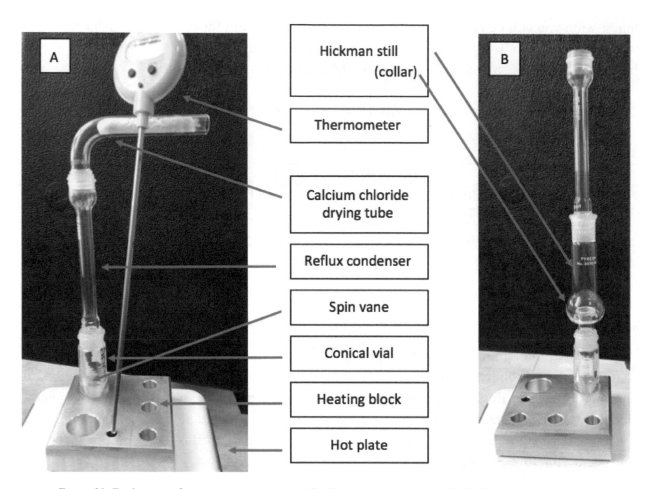

	Hickman still (collar)
	Thermometer
	Calcium chloride drying tube
	Reflux condenser
	Spin vane
	Conical vial
	Heating block
	Hot plate

Figure 31. Fischer esterification reaction set-up. A) Synthesis apparatus set-up. B) Distillation apparatus setup

Experimental procedure: product isolation

Transfer solution mixture to a clean, large test tube using a Pasteur pipette. Extract the solution mixture in the test tube three times using 2 mL portions of 5% sodium bicarbonate solution each time (TA will quickly demonstrate you the extraction technique before you proceed. This will be done while you reflux your reaction mixture). During each extraction step, remove the bottom aqueous layer using a Pasteur pipette and discard it. Finally, after sodium bicarbonate extraction, add 1 mL of deionized water to your solution mixture. Next, cover the test tube with parafilm, vortex it for 30-60 s. Remove the parafilm and wait until two layers separate. After that, transfer the (top) organic layer to 10 mL Erlenmayer flask. Prepare a Pasteur filter pipette by putting a small cotton ball inside it and a 2 cm layer of anhydrous Na_2SO_4 to capture the remaining water (TA will demonstrate it). Finally, using another Pasteur pipette run your organic extract through the prepared Pasteur pipette and collect the filtrate in microcentrifuge tube. Cap the tube, insert in into conical vial and place securely into drawer.

The purification of your ester (from crude product mixture) will be carried out by simple distillation. You will have to prepare the distillation set-up composed of 5 mL conical vial with boiling stone, Hickman still and air condenser (see Figure 31B).

Using a Pasteur pipette transfer crude ester extract to a 5 mL conical vial containing a boiling stone. Next, attach the vial containing the crude ester to Hickman still equipped with an air condenser. Place this set-up on a hot plate to perform distillation. Distill your unknown ester by slowly increasing the temperature to 130-160 °C. Remember that your crude reaction mixture contains also diethyl ether which has a low boiling point. Your ester distillate will collect in the collar of Hickman still (Figure 31B). After distillation is complete transfer your ester using Pasteur pipette to a clean and tared vial. Weigh vial containing the collected distillate to determine the mass of your product. Record yield of your pure ester product.

Obtain from TA the IR, ^{13}C NMR, ^{1}H NMR spectra and proceed with their analysis in the lab. This can be done while waiting for distillation to be finished. Record all your findings directly in the notebook (not on a separate sheets). TA will verify your work at the end of lab session and will sign your notebook. The analysis of the IR/NMR signals must be done in a typical way using a table format (typical column description applies).

What is expected on the report

All standard lab report sections apply. Please see chapter 7 for details. More specifically, the following items are also required:

Introduction

Provide background information on the theoretical problems:
- What are esters' role in nature (provide at least three examples); how to synthesize them (why Fischer esterification method was used? Any advantage of using this synthetic method?)

Results and discussion

Please to remember to reference all your spectra/images/tables in the text. Do not forget to make figure captions.

Results:
- Identify your unknown alcohol and ester. Provide their common or IUPAC names.
- Actual ester yield (calculations in your <u>lab notebook</u> must be present, re-type it in the report).
- Theoretical yield (calculations in your <u>lab notebook</u> must be present, re-type it in the report).

- Percent yield (calculations in your <u>lab notebook</u> must be present, re-type it in the report).
- IR spectrum analysis (report your IR data in a table format), draw structure of your compound on all your spectra. <u>Attach original spectra at the end of your report.</u>
- ^{13}C NMR spectrum analysis. Label of all carbon signals *1...n* on ^{13}C NMR spectrum and report NMR data in a table format. Draw structure of your compound on all your spectra. <u>Attach original spectra at the end of your report.</u>
- ^{1}H NMR spectrum analysis. Label of all carbon signals *A...Z* on ^{1}H NMR spectrum and report NMR data in a table format. Draw structure of your compound on all your spectra. <u>Attach original spectra at the end of your report.</u>
- Chemdoodle drawn Fischer esterification reaction mechanism using <u>your identified alcohol</u> and acetic acid (lone electron pairs, arrows, electron flow). Paste this into your MS Word report (this section). Lack of this computer-drawn mechanism or its falsification will result in a lack of credit for this section.
- Report the appearance of your product (any aroma?)

Discussion:
- Discussion of reaction yields (low/high?), synthetic problems etc. How would you improve the yield of this reaction?
- Discussion of your signals (NMR and IR) and relationship between observed and literature values for your identified peaks (similarities/differences, overlaps...etc). Do not simply mentioned them – discuss your reasoning in structure elucidation.
- Where is your identified ester found in nature?

Use IR peak tables from Appendix. However, once you have identified your compound, for even better comparison with literature values you could search various chemical databases to further confirm your findings.

Conclusion(s)

Summarize the main features of the report, the objectives, findings and conclusions. You briefly explain any possible sources of error relevant to your results. Have you successfully performed the experiment? Why/why not? Was your synthesis/purification/analysis successful (yield...)?

References

Please cite any references in ACS format. Remember to cite every source that helped you. Citation of other college/common websites are forbidden as they are not the valid source of information. DO NOT cite this manual, other courses' websites, only original works! Only primary citation sources such as journals and books will give you a full credit.

Your complete lab report must include
1. Hard copy of your lab report & online submission.
2. Original pages from your lab notebook. Pages cannot be loose. You must staple/bind them before submission.
3. Attach original IR/NMR spectra and original pages from your lab notebook to a hard copy report.

Please pay attention to report deadlines. See Canvas for details.

Nitration of phenol and separation of nitrophenols

Purpose

In this experiment students will explore an electrophilic aromatic substitution reaction. A phenol will be nitrated under mild conditions using a dilute nitric acid method. The reaction will yield a mixture of *o*-nitrophenol and *p*-nitrophenol as well as traces of 2,4-dinitrophenol and 2,4,6-trinitrophenol. The crude reaction mixture will be submitted for column chromatography separation (purification) to obtain pure *o*- and *p*-nitrophenols. The purification process will be monitored by TLC. The obtained nitrophenols will be further analyzed using IR and NMR spectroscopy.

Number of laboratory sessions: 3

Background information

The elctrophilic aromatic substitution reaction involves substitution of hydrogen atom from an aromatic ring with an electrophile. The reaction proceeds in two steps. At first, the π electrons of aromatic benzene ring attack the electrophile forming a resonance stabilized carbocation. This is a very slow process, requiring energy due to a loss of aromaticity. In the second step, the carbocation intermediate is attacked by a base and loses a proton. These electrons are used to rebuild a π bond and restore the aromaticity. As opposed to the first step, this step is fast and exergonic because aromaticity of the ring is regained. In this laboratory experiment you will perform a nitration of a phenol (Figure 32).

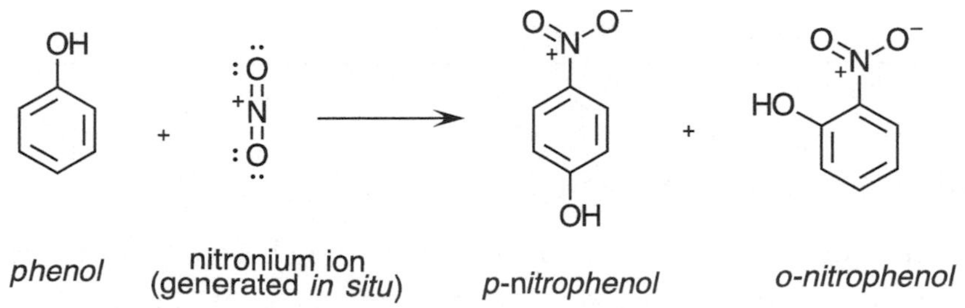

Figure 32. Phenol nitration reaction.

You will use diluted (30%) nitric acid, which will be a source of generated *in situ* nitronium ion. After completion of the reaction you will isolate crude products and separate it using column chromatography technique. The efficiency of purification will be monitored by thin-layer chromatography analysis. Your products will be then characterized by IR and NMR spectroscopy.

Pre-lab preparation

In your lab notebook, prepare the following (see lab notebook guide for details):
1. Draw a flowchart showing all procedures required for this experiment. Prepare it so that it can be used as a sole source of your experimental procedures.
2. Detailed, hand-written reaction mechanisms of *ortho-* and *para-* nitration reaction (separately). Must include arrows, electron flow and lone pairs.
3. Hand written table of chemicals that include physicochemical data for **all** chemicals used (see chapter 6).
4. Theoretical yield calculations. Is it possible to calculate the theoretical yield ?
5. Drawings of all the glassware and instrumentation used for the experiment. Glassware must be properly named.

In the laboratory

Here is how the experiment will be performed. In the first lab session you will perform nitration reaction and isolation of crude nitrophenols. In the second lab session you will separate *o-* and *p-* nitrophenols using column chromatography. In the last session you will analyze your product fractions by TLC analysis and then characterize your pure *o-* and *p-*nitrophenols by IR and ^{1}H NMR spectroscopy.

The essential reactants for nitrophenol synthesis are provided in Table 1.

Table 1.

Reactants used					
Compound	**MW**	**amount used**	**mmol**	**mp (°C)**	**bp (°C)**
Nitric acid, diluted (30%)		2.5 mL			
Phenol	94.11	94 mg		42	182

Experimental procedure: nitration reaction

Prepare your magnetic stirrer by placing it under the fume hood. To a 5 mL conical vial weigh and add 94 mg of phenol. When transferring your sample around the lab, keep your vial capped (using cap or finger) as phenol's smell is unpleasant. Insert spin vane into your reaction vessel and attach the air condenser to the conical vial placed on a stirrer. **IMPORTANT: Turn on spinning before proceeding with next step.** Next, using graduated measuring cylinder add 2.5 mL of diluted nitric acid (30 %) to a clean 10 mL Erlenmeyer flask. Add the 2.5 mL of diluted nitric acid **slowly – dropwise** – using Pasteur pipette through the top of air condenser to your 5 mL conical vial containing phenol. Stir the resulting reaction mixture at room temperature for 20 min.

Experimental procedure: crude product isolation

Add 1 mL of ice-cold deionized water to your brown reaction mixture. Remove the spin vane from the 5 mL reaction vial using magnetic wand. Transfer diluted reaction mixture to a large test tube. Extract the diluted reaction mixture in the test tube with three portions of 2 mL each of dichloromethane (DCM). This means that each time after you add 2 mL of DCM you will (1) cover your tube with parafilm, (2) vortex it thoroughly (~30 sec.), (3) carefully remove the parafilm, (4) wait until two layers separate, (5) remove the bottom organic layer, (6) using Pasteur pipette, transfer the organic layer to a 10 mL Erlenmeyer flask containing approximately 250 mg of sodium sulfate (do not weigh). After three extractions, you will have ~6 mL of the organic extract in the 10 mL Erlenmeyer flask. Gently swirl the Erlenmeyer flask and let sodium sulfate remove the remaining water. Prepare the Pasteur pipette filter. Next filter your organic extract to another clean 25 mL Erlenmeyer flask. Wash the remaining Na_2SO_4 in the 10 mL Erlenmeyer flask with an additional 1 mL of DCM, and filter this solution into the 25 mL Erlenmeyer flask containing the dried extracts. At this stage of the experiment, label your 25 mL Erlenmeyer flask and leave it uncovered and secured in your drawer.

Before proceeding to the next step prepare 10 scintillation vials (wash them with acetone) for fractions to be collected during column chromatography separation.

Experimental procedure: product purification and characterization

Packing of the chromatographic column

Using provided weighing boats, weigh 7 g of silica gel (70-230 mesh) and transfer it to a 100 mL volume (or similar) beaker. To that beaker, using graduate cylinder, add 30 mL of solvent composed of 60:40 DCM/hexanes. Using stirring rod or thicker end of Pasteur pipette stir that mixture until homogenous slurry is obtained. While swelling silica gel, proceed with column set-up. Prepare the column by packing it with a small cotton plug at the bottom of it. Next add small amount of sand so that it forms 5-10 mm layer. Make sure that the valve is closed and fix it on a stand. While stirring the silica slurry, pour it through the funnel into the column (make sure that you don't overfill it). Open the bottom valve and let the solvent drip to a beaker containing the slurry reservoir. You will recycle the solvent so that all the silica slurry is transferred to the column. The silica gel will be settling down. Tap the column gently from the side using a spatula to help the silica to settle. Once the solvent level is approximately 1 inch above the silica level stop the flow and transfer the remaining slurry again on the top of the column, and open the valve to let it drip (but collect the solvent!). Continue slurry pouring/solvent recycling until all silica is transferred to the column. Once it's done, a 10 mm layer of the solvent must remain at the top of the column. Next, using a funnel, pour 5-10 mm layer of sand. Tap the column from the side to let it settle. Add another 5 mL of the 60:40 DCM/hexanes and let it run through the column. Reduce the top layer of the remaining solvent to only 2-3 mm above the sand level (do not let the column run dry). At this point your column is packed and ready for use.

Chromatographic separation of nitrophenols

Your crude reaction extract should be a solid. Using a Pasteur pipette add 1 mL of 60:40 DCM/hexanes to your reaction mixture to dissolve it. Apply that crude solution on the top of the column. Open the bottom valve and let the crude sample adsorb at the top of the column (sink-in). Once you reach a 2-3 mm solvent level above the silica, stop the flow again. Add another 1 mL of DCM/hexanes solution to wash the vial containing the crude mixture and transfer the remaining sample to the column again. Let it soak in.

DO NOT discard the small remaining amount of your crude reaction mixture as it will be used for TLC analysis in the next lab.

Next, using clean Pasteur pipette add ~6 mL of DCM/hexanes solution and run it through the column. You should be collecting the eluent in a waste beaker at this point. A yellow band(s) traveling down the column should be visible (see Figure 33). Keep adding small portions of **fresh** DCM/hexanes solvent as it runs through the column. Start collecting first moving yellow band into vial and label it as "#1". Continue to run the column with ~ 4 mL portions of 60:40 DCM/hexanes applied on the column. Change vials for every ~5 mL fraction of solvent collected until a total of 3 fractions are collected (vials #1 - #3). Next, collect ~4 mL fractions #4, #5 and #6. Stop the flow when needed: during vial switching or solvent addition. After first 5 fractions are collected, switch solvent system. Add ~6 mL of 50:50 DCM/EtOAc on top of the column. Open the flow and keep collecting ~4 mL fractions into next vials numbered #7 through #10. The idea is to separate the two isomers (yellow bands) into several vials, which in turn will be analyzed by TLC. TLC will show you if you have successfully separated your nitration products.

Leave your uncapped vials containing collected fractions secured in your drawer. The solvent will evaporate and crystalline product will be obtained. You will proceed with fraction analysis in the next laboratory session.

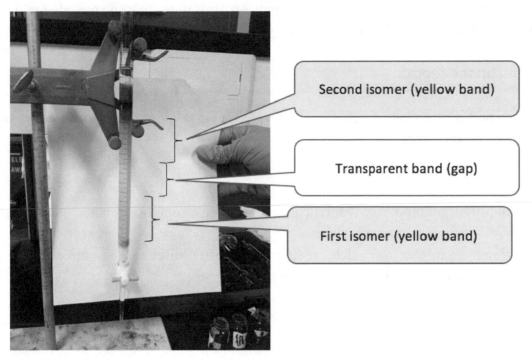

Figure 33. Column chromatography - separation of nitrophenols Observe two yellow bands corresponding to two isomers.

Experimental procedure: fraction analysis and compound identification

Perform TLC analysis of your fractions #1 - #10 to assess the purity of the collected fractions. As a solvent system use 80:20 hexanes/EtOAc. Use 2 separate plates, and spot fractions #1 - #5 on plate 1 and fractions #6-#10 on plate 2. Remember to spot your crude reaction mixture as a reference (on both plates) as well. See Figure 34 for a sample TLC plate layout.

Mark your spots, redraw the image of TLC plates in your lab notebook and calculate R_f values of your *o*- and *p*-nitrophenols. Keep your plates in the drawer.

While waiting for TLC analysis empty the solvent from your column (let it drip to dryness, dispose liquid waste) and give it to your TA for disposal.

Rx - *reaction mixture*

Figure 34. Sample TLC plate layout.

- Record IR spectrum of your isolated *o-* *and/or* *p*-nitrophenol isomers. Perform peak analysis.
- Print out provided ^{1}H NMR spectra of *o*- and *p*-nitrophenols (spectra provided on Canvas). Analyze the peaks. Observe similarities/differences between the spectra. Analysis must be

done in majority in the lab during this lab session. Analysis notes must be included in your lab notebook. Also, all analyses must be discussed in your report.

What is expected on the report

All standard lab report sections apply. Please see chapter 7 for details. More specifically, the following items are also required:

Introduction

Provide background information on the theoretical problem - electrophilic aromatic substitution reaction:
- provide three examples of such reactions. Briefly discuss the directing and activating/deactivating effects of different functional groups.

Results and discussion

Please to remember to reference all your spectra/images/tables in the text. Do not forget to make figure captions.

Results:
- Report Reaction yields (calculations) for both *o-* and *p-* isomers.
- Report Chemdoodle-redrawn TLC plates from your fraction analysis.
- Report TLC plate analysis and discussion of column chromatography purification.
- Include table containing mass of #1-#10 fractions.
- Report IR and NMR spectra analysis (report your data in a usual table format), draw structure of your compound on all your spectra. Attach the original spectra at the end of your report.

Discussion:
- Discussion of reaction yields, synthetic/purification problems etc., key for this experiment.
- Discuss success/failure of column chromatography purification based on TLC analysis.
- Discussion of polarity for both isomers. Explain where the differences come from.
- In your discussion explain why *p*-nitrophenol is a stronger acid than phenol itself? Fully explain using **Chemdoodle drawn** resonance forms.
- Discuss similarities and differences of your obtained/expected spectral data.
- Discussion of your IR/^{1}H NMR signals and relationship between observed and literature values for your identified peaks (similarities/differences, overlaps...etc).

Conclusion(s)

Summarize the main features of the report, the objectives, findings and conclusions. You briefly explain any possible sources of error relevant to your results. Have you successfully performed the experiment? Why/why not? Was your synthesis/purification/analysis successful (yield…)?

References

Please cite any references in ACS format. Remember to cite every source that helped you. Citation of other college/common websites are forbidden as they are not the valid source of information. DO NOT cite this manual, other courses' websites, only original works! Only primary citation sources such as journals and books will give you a full credit.

Report submission

Your complete lab report must include
1. Hard copy of your lab report & online submission.
2. Original pages from your lab notebook. Pages cannot be loose. You must staple/bind them before submission.
3. Attach original IR/NMR spectra and original pages from your lab notebook to a hard copy report.

Please pay attention to report deadlines. See Canvas for details.

Synthesis and characterization of azo dye: methyl orange

Purpose

In this experiment students will explore diazotization reaction to obtain methyl orange. The newly synthesized azo dye - 4-[4-(Dimethylamino)phenylazo]benzenesulfonic acid (methyl orange) is formed upon coupling of diazotized sulfanilic acid with N,N-dimethylaniline in a weekly acidic solution. Methyl orange is commonly used as a dye and pH indicator and successful synthesis will confirm its activity at different pH and the ability to dye cotton and nylon-6,6 polymers.

Number of laboratory sessions: 2

Background information

Dyes and pigments are important industrial chemicals. They can color fibers permanently, such that they will not lose this color when exposed to sweat, light, water and many chemical substances. The world's first commercially successful synthetic dye - mauveine, was discovered by accident in 1856 by William H. Perkin (at the age of 18). By the end of the 19th century, over ten thousand synthetic dyes had been developed and used for manufacturing purposes.

Azo dyes are diazotized amines coupled to an amine or phenol, with one or more azo bonds (–N=N–). They are synthetic compounds and account for more than 50% of all the dyes produced annually, showing the largest spectrum of colors.[1] Nearly all the dyestuffs used by the textile industry are azo dyes, and they are also widely used in the printing, food, papermaking and cosmetic industries.[2]

Azo compounds are compounds having azo group R-N=N-R' in which R and R' can be either aryl or alkyl group. The simplest example of an aryl azo compound is azobenzene (Figure 35).

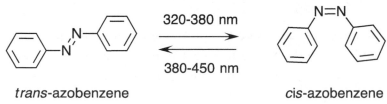

trans-azobenzene   *cis*-azobenzene

Figure 35. Azobenzene photoisomerization.

One of the most intriguing properties of azobenzene and other azo compounds is the photoisomerization of cis/trans isomers. The two isomers can be switched with particular wavelengths of light (Figure 35).

Because of π-delocalization, aryl azo compounds have rich colors, especially reds, oranges, and yellows. Therefore, they are used as dyes, and are commonly known as azo dyes.

Azo compounds are important to our society not only in colorization of fabrics. Some DVD-R/+R and some CD-R discs use blue azo dye as the recording layer. Azo pigments consist of colorless minerals as carriers colored using an azo compound. Azo pigments are important in a variety of paints including artist's paints.

Azo compounds can be obtained in a "one-pot", two step reaction (Figure 36). You are to synthesize the one of the azo compounds – methyl orange. This compound dye wool, silk and skin, and you must work carefully to avoid getting them on your hands or clothes. The dye will eventually wear off your hands after some time.

The reaction starts by diazotization of sulfanilic acid with sodium nitrite. The diazonium salt is then immediately used to react with N,N-dimethylaniline in an reaction of electrophilic aromatic substitution to form methyl orange.

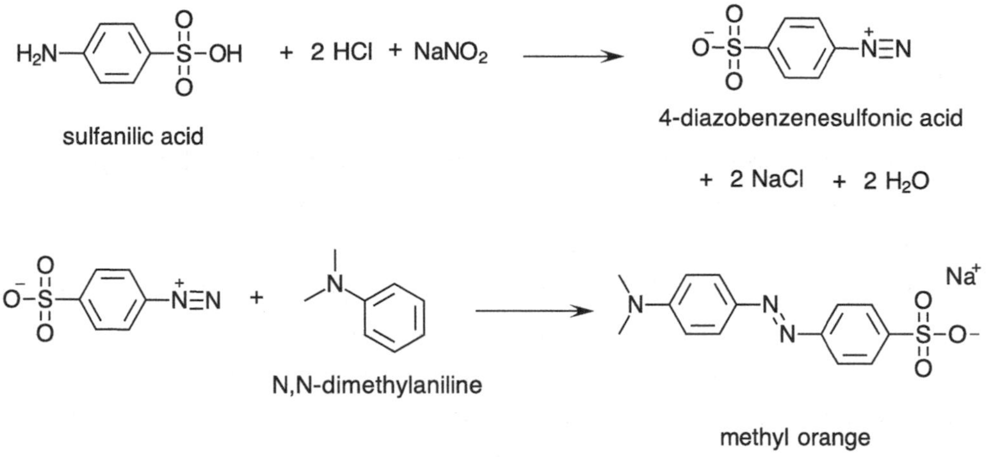

Figure 36. Synthesis of methyl orange.

NOTE:

The diazonium salts are unstable at temperatures above 5 °C even in solution. That's why they are generated *in situ* and used immediately in the next reaction. At higher temperatures and in the dry form, the diazo group decomposes violently decompose to produce N_2 (explosive!).

The diazotization reaction is possible due to a nitrosonium ion NO^+), which is generated *in situ* from hydrochloric acid and sodium nitrite. Next, amino group of sulfanilic acid reacts with nitrosonium ion to form 4-diazobenzenesulfonic acid. The latter one reacts rapidly with N,N-dimethylaniline to give methyl orange.

Pre-lab preparation

In your lab notebook, prepare the following (see lab notebook guide for details):
1. Draw a flowchart showing all procedures required for this experiment. Prepare it so that it can be used as a sole source of your experimental procedures.
2. Detailed, hand-written reaction mechanism of methyl orange synthesis starting from sulfanilic acid, sodium salt and nitrosonium ion. You must include arrows, electron flow and lone pairs.
3. Hand written table of chemicals that include physicochemical data for **all** chemicals used (see chapter 6).
4. Theoretical yield calculations.
5. Drawings of all the glassware and instrumentation used for the experiment. Glassware must be properly named.
6. Why does the dimethylaniline couple with the diazonium salt at the para position of the ring? Explain in writing (in your lab notebook) and support your answer with written resonance forms.

In the laboratory

The essential reactants for methyl orange synthesis are provided in Table 1.

Table 1.

Reactants used					
Compound	MW	amount used	mmol	mp (°C)	d (g/mL)
Sulfanilic acid	173.19	85 mg		288	
Sodium nitrite	68.99	50 mg		271	182
3 % Na_2CO_3	105.98	1 mL			
HCl (concentrated)	36.46	0.125 mL			1.49
Dimethylaniline	121.18	75 mg			0.956
Acetic acid	60.05	65 mg			1.049
10 % NaOH solution	40				
10 % HCl solution	36.46				
10% sodium sulfate		0.5 mL			
10% of H_2SO_4		5 drops			

Experimental procedure: diazotization of sulfanilic acid

Weight out 85 mg of sulfanilic acid and place it into the 4 mL conical vial equipped with a spin vane. Add 1 mL of 3% aqueous solution of Na_2CO_3. Sulfanilic acid dissolves and react with base to form a salt. Stir that solution at room temp. for several minutes, until CO_2 bubbles are no longer produced. To that solution add 50 mg of $NaNO_2$. Stir that solution until sodium nitrite is dissolved completely. Next, transfer this solution onto ice bath (small beaker or crystallization dish can be used). Cool that solution on ice (keep it there) and add to it ~1 mL of ice chunk (not more). Next, add 0.125 mL of concentrated HCl. Keep this solution on ice. If upon addition of HCl a brown color appears (what is the source of it?). Stir reaction mixture for few seconds on a stirrer and the color should disappear (put it back on ice). After the white precipitate is formed, wait another 5 min. before proceeding with the next step. If precipitate does not appear, add another portion of concentrated HCl.

Experimental procedure: electrophilic aromatic substitution

Obtain 75 mg of N,N-dimethylaniline and 65 mg of acetic acid (you have to convert mass units to volume first). Mix them together in a separate conical vial. Using Pasteur pipette, transfer that mixture to the vial containing white precipitate of diazotized sulfanilic acid. Use few drops of water to rinse out all the dimethylaniline and acetic acid and transfer it to reaction mixture. Stir mixture vigorously using magnetic spin vane. A red paste appears after few minutes. Continue to stir that reaction mixture for another 10-15 min. After that time add 1 mL of 10% NaOH to convert methyl orange into its sodium salt. Upon addition of NaOH a deep green color should appear. Stir that solution for another 5 min. A thick green-brown paste containing methyl orange sodium salt is formed.

Experimental procedure: product isolation

Collect crude product using vacuum filtration on a Hirsch funnel equipped additionally with filtering paper (ask TA for it). A thick paste should remain on the filter. Use saturated sodium chloride solution (1-2 mL) to rinse off the reaction vial and wash the filter. Using a spatula transfer the product from the filter into new (pre-weighted) conical vial (be careful, this step could be messy!). Put the product containing vial into the oven for 15 min in order to dry it. The paste solidifies. After cooling down the vial from the oven, weigh it and estimate the yield.

Cleaning up the laboratory workspace

Combined filtrates should be placed into hazardous waste container. Highly colored filtrates from the reaction are very water soluble. After dilution, it with a large quantity of water they can be flushed down the drain since the amount of solid is small.

Take small amount (tiny spec) of your obtained methyl orange and put in into a test tube. Add 1 mL of 10% of NaOH solution. Observe the color. Next using Pasteur pipette start adding dropwise a 10 % of HCl solution. Observe color change. Up to 1.5 mL of HCl could be used. Record all your observations in a notebook. The color change occurs pH > 4.4 (yellow) and below pH < 3.2.

Experimental procedure: dyeing of cotton and nylon-6,6 fibers

Prepare the dye bath by adding 50 mg of methyl orange, 0.5 mL of 10% sodium sulfate, 15 mL of water and 5 drops of 10% of sulfuric acid. A 50 mL (or similar) beaker could be used for this purpose. Place that beaker onto a hot plate (under the fume hood) and start heating it. Place a piece of cotton ball (1-inch diameter) for 10 min at a temperature near the boiling point. Remove the cotton from the dye bath using tweezers and put it onto a paper towel to cool down. Once cool, wash it under running water before drying it.

Perform analogous step using nylon-6,6 obtained in a prior experiment.

Dry both polymers and compare the results using white sheet of paper as a background. Are there any differences in color between the two fibers?

Cleaning up the laboratory workspace

Residues of methyl orange must be placed into hazardous waste container. Wash your glassware thoroughly with hot water until clean.

What is expected on the report

All standard lab report sections apply. Please see chapter 7 for details. More specifically, the following items are also required:

Introduction

Provide background information on the theoretical problem - electrophilic aromatic:
- The application of diazotization reaction in organic chemistry. What is Sandmeyer reaction? Provide example.

Results and discussion

Please to remember to reference all your spectra/images/tables in the text. Do not forget to make figure captions.

    Results:
- Report reaction yields – theoretical and actual.
- Report the physicochemical properties of your synthesized compound.

- Provide Chemdoodle drawn formulas for two methyl orange forms – acidic and basic. Charges and lone electron pairs must be present.
- Report dyeing results in a table format.

Discussion:
- Explain why melting point of the product was not determined in the laboratory?
- Discussion of reaction yields, synthetic/purification problems etc., key for this experiment.
- Provide detailed (molecular) explanation on why the dyeing of the two polymers were different/similar. Discuss similarities and differences of your obtained/expected spectral data.
- Propose a chemical reaction (use Chemdoodle) that would lead to complete discoloration of methyl orange.

Conclusion(s)

Summarize the main features of the report, the objectives, findings and conclusions. You briefly explain any possible sources of error relevant to your results. Have you successfully performed the experiment? Why/why not? Was your synthesis/purification/analysis successful (yield…)?

References

Please cite any references in ACS format. Remember to cite every source that helped you. Citation of other college/common websites are forbidden as they are not the valid source of information. DO NOT cite this manual, other courses' websites, only original works! Only primary citation sources such as journals and books will give you a full credit.

Report submission

Your complete lab report must include
1. Hard copy of your lab report & online submission.
2. Original pages from your lab notebook. Pages cannot be loose. You must staple/bind them before submission.
3. Attach original IR/NMR spectra and original pages from your lab notebook to a hard copy report.

Please pay attention to report deadlines. See Canvas for details.

Literature

(1)   Carliell, C. M.; Barclay, S. J.; Naidoo, N.; Buckley, C. A.; Mulholland, D. A.; Senior, E. Microbial Decolourisation of a Reactive Azo Dye under Anaerobic Conditions. *Water SA* **1995**, *21* (1), 61–69.
(2)   Chang, J. S.; Chou, C.; Lin, Y. C.; Lin, P. J.; Ho, J. Y.; Lee Hu, T. Kinetic Characteristics of Bacterial Azo-Dye Decolorization by Pseudomonas Luteola. *Water Res.* **2001**, *35* (12), 2841–2850.

Conversion of L-Phenylalanine to L-phenyllactic acid

Purpose

In this experiment students will perform the conversion of L-phenylalanine (L-Phe) into L-phenyllactic acid using two S_N2 reactions. Phenylalanine is a readily available and optically active organic compound. It is also one of the 20 naturally occurring amino acids. In a one-pot manner and tandem S_N2 reactions, it is conveniently transformed into α-hydroxy acid in a stereospecific way.

Number of laboratory sessions: 2

Background information

α-amino acids can be transformed into their corresponding α-hydroxy acids in a diazotization reaction and subsequent two S_N2 reactions (Figure 37).

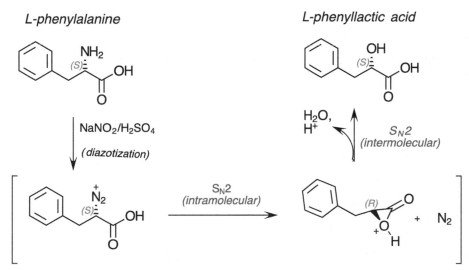

Figure 37. Transformation of L-Phe into L-phenyllactic acid via tandem S_N2 reactions

Diazotization of L-phenylalanine using sodium nitrite under acidic conditions results in the formation of an unstable diazonium salt, which undergoes rapid intramolecular S_N2 reaction to give highly constrained α-lactone. This internal ester, upon hydrolysis in water undergoes a slow intramolecular S_N2 reaction to yield α-hydroxy acid: (S)-2-hydroxy-3-phenylpropanoic acid (L-phenyllactic acid). Since this overall reaction is composed of tandem S_N2 reactions, the product retains the same configuration ($S \rightarrow R \rightarrow S$).

This reaction is environmentally friendly – it runs in aqueous solution, uses natural amino acid as reactant and generates no hazardous waste requiring disposal.

The starting amino acid, L-Phe is soluble under the acidic solution. Upon cooling and addition of $NaNO_2$ and with stirring, tiny bubbles of N_2 gas become appear as diazonium salt is formed and undergoes rapid intramolecular S_N2 reaction. This reaction is typically finished in an hour after warming it back to room temperature. The second, intermolecular S_N2 reaction is much slower and requires 24-48 h to complete. During that time, product which is formed, precipitates from the solution as white crystalline substance. The difference in solubility, between the starting, amphoteric amino acid and the final α-hydroxy acid is apparent. Product is isolated by Hirsch funnel filtration and further characterized by IR and melting point analysis.

Pre-lab preparation

In your lab notebook, prepare the following (see lab notebook guide for details):
1. Draw a flowchart showing all procedures required for this experiment. Prepare it so that it can be used as a sole source of your experimental procedures.
2. Detailed, hand-written reaction mechanism of L-phenyllactic acid formation. You must include arrows, electron flow and lone pairs.
3. Hand written table of chemicals that include physicochemical data for **all** chemicals used (see chapter 6).
4. Theoretical yield calculations.
5. Drawings of all the glassware and instrumentation used for the experiment. Glassware must be properly named.
6. Why does the dimethylaniline couple with the diazonium salt at the para position of the ring? Explain in writing (in your lab notebook) and support your answer with written resonance forms.

In the laboratory

You will have two laboratory sessions to complete this experiment:
- In the first lab session, you will perform the diazotization reaction.
- In the second lab session, you will perform product isolation and characterization by IR spectroscopy and m.p. analysis.

The essential reactants for L-phenyllactic synthesis are provided in Table 1.

Table 1.

Reactants used					
Compound	MW	amount used	mmol	mp (°C)	bp (°C)
L-phenylalanine	165.19		1	283	
1M H_2SO_4	98.09	0.75 mL			
3M $NaNO_2$	68.99	0.5 mL			

Experimental procedure: reaction setup

Prepare your magnetic stirrer by placing it under the fume hood. To a 5 mL conical vial weigh and add 1 mmol of L-phenylalanine (L-Phe). Insert a spin vane, add 0.75 mL of 1M H_2SO_4 solution and stir it at room temperature until amino acid completely dissolves.

Prepare an ice-bath and cool the L-Phe solution to < 5 ^{0}C (use thermometer). Once the solution is cooled, add first portion - 50 μL of 3M $NaNO_2$. There will be a total of 10 additions of 50 μL aliquots of sodium nitrite over a period of 1 hour. You will have to work with your TA on pace of the addition. A slow rate of addition is important for a good reaction yield. Once addition is complete, remove the vial from the ice bath and let solution stir until the end of the lab period. Lightly wrap the reaction vial using parafilm and leave it until next lab period.

Experimental procedure: crude product isolation

Assemble the Hirsch funnel filtration set-up. Prepare a vial containing ice-cold water. Before filtration, cool the product containing vial on ice-bath and then isolate the product by a Hirsch funnel. Wash the filtrate with cold water (once) and then with dichloromethane (2 portions, 1 mL each). Collect the crystals and place them into pre-weighted vial. Allow the crystals to dry at room temperature (15 min) before characterization. Record obtained yield.

Product characterization

L-phenyllactic acid will be characterized by IR and m.p. analyses. Perform IR spectra acquisition and analysis. Record m.p. and report it.

What is expected on the report

All standard lab report sections apply. Please see chapter 7 for details. More specifically, the following items are also required:

Introduction

Provide background information on the theoretical problem - S_n2 reactions. What are the most efficient reaction conditions to perform such reaction?

Results and discussion

Please to remember to reference all your spectra/images/tables in the text. Do not forget to make figure captions.

Results:
- Report reaction yields – theoretical and actual.
- m. p. analysis.
- IR spectrum analysis.
- Report dyeing results in a table format.

Discussion:
- Discussion of reaction yields, synthetic/purification problems etc., key for this experiment.
- Discuss the relationship of chiral substrate and product.
- In your discussion hypothesize, based on above reaction conditions what (and why) other natural amino acids could be used to obtain corresponding alpha-hydroxy acids without any method modification.
- Discuss similarities and differences of your obtained/expected spectral and m.p. data, as compared with literature.
- Discuss what is the possible practical application of synthesized L-phenyllactic acid.

Conclusion(s)

Summarize the main features of the report, the objectives, findings and conclusions. You briefly explain any possible sources of error relevant to your results. Have you successfully performed the experiment? Why/why not? Was your synthesis/purification/analysis successful (yield…)?

References

Please cite any references in ACS format. Remember to cite every source that helped you. Citation of other college/common websites are forbidden as they are not the valid source of information.

DO NOT cite this manual, other courses' websites, only original works! Only primary citation sources such as journals and books will give you a full credit.

Report submission

Your complete lab report must include
1. Hard copy of your lab report & online submission.
2. Original pages from your lab notebook. Pages cannot be loose. You must staple/bind them before submission.
3. Attach original IR/NMR spectra and original pages from your lab notebook to a hard copy report.

Please pay attention to report deadlines. See Canvas for details.

Synthesis and characterization of dibenzalacetone

Purpose

this experiment you will synthesize dibenzalacetone by using aldol condensation reaction. The product will then be recrystallized and characterized by m.p. and IR analysis.

Number of laboratory sessions: 1

Background information

The reaction of an aldehyde with a ketone is the aldol condensation reaction. A mixed aldol condensation reaction using sodium hydroxide is called Claisen-Schmidt reaction.

In this laboratory exercise, you will synthesize dibenzalacetone by condensation of two equivalents of benzaldehyde with one equivalent of acetone. The aldehyde carbonyl is more reactive than that of the ketone and therefore reacts rapidly with the anion of the ketone to give b-hydroxyketone, which easily undergoes base-catalyzed dehydratation (Figure 38). By varying the amounts of the reactants in this Claisen-Schmidt reaction it is possible to obtain either the mono- or di-substituted benzalacetone. We will prepare dibenzalacetone, which is easier to isolate from reaction mixture.

In the present experiment, sufficient amount of ethanol is present as a solvent to dissolve the starting material, benzaldehyde and it's intermediate – benzalacetone. Benzalacetone undergoes second condensation reaction forming final product – dibenzalacetone.

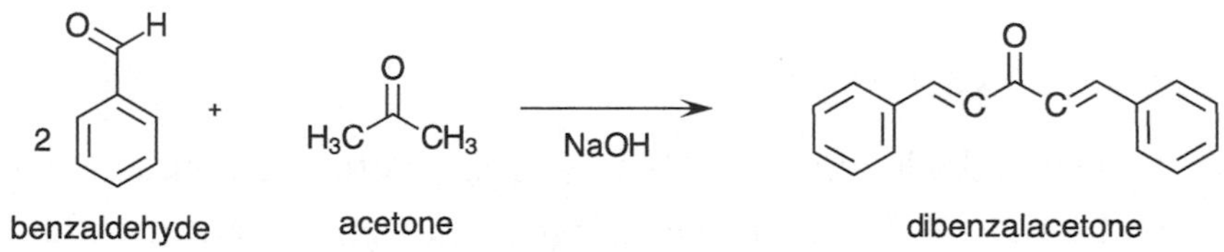

Figure 38. The overall reaction scheme for dibenzalacetone synthesis.

The synthesized dibenzalacetone will be collected by Hirsch funnel filtration, recrystallized from ethanol and further characterized.

Pre-lab preparation

In your lab notebook, prepare the following (see lab notebook guide for details):
1. Draw a flowchart showing all procedures required for this experiment. Prepare it so that it can be used as a sole source of your experimental procedures.
2. Detailed, hand-written reaction mechanism. You must include arrows, electron flow and lone pairs.
3. Hand written table of chemicals that include physicochemical data for **all** chemicals used (see chapter 6).
4. Theoretical yield calculations.
5. Drawings of all the glassware and instrumentation used for the experiment. Glassware must be properly named.
6. Why does the dimethylaniline couple with the diazonium salt at the para position of the ring? Explain in writing (in your lab notebook) and support your answer with written resonance forms.

In the laboratory

The essential reactants for dibenzalacetone synthesis are provided in Table 1.

Table 1.

Reactants used					
Compound	MW	amount used	mmol	bp (°C)	d (g/mL)
benzaldehyde	106.04	212 μL		178	1.04
acetone	58.08	74 μL		56	0.79
95% ethanol	46.07	1.5 mL		78	0.78
10% NaOH		2 mL			

Experimental procedure: reaction setup

To a 4 mL conical vial add 2mL of 10% of sodium hydroxide solution and a magnetic spin vane. Next, add 1.5 mL mL of 95% ethanol and stir it on a magnetic stirrer. After that, add 212 μL of benzaldehyde and keep stirring. The benzaldehyde initially insoluble will go into solution and a clear (pale yellow) solution is obtained. Next, add 74 μL of acetone and continue to stir. At some point, a yellow solid should form. Continue stirring the reaction mixture vigorously for another 30 min. At the end of that time, yellow, flaky crystals should be observed. After that time, cool the reaction mixture in an ice bath and isolate the product by vacuum filtration using Hirsch funnel.

Wash it 2 times with ice-cold water (using Pasteur pipette). Weigh and record the amount of your crude product.

Next, prepare water bath. To a 100 mL beaker add 20 mL of water and heat it on the hot plate until almost boiling point. Prepare a separate tube, add ~2 mL of ethanol to it and heat it in water bath. Transfer your product into large test tube. Using a minimal amount of hot ethanol (from your hot ethanol tube) dissolve your dibenzalacetone. You will want to keep your tube in a water bath while dissolving the product. After you obtain a clear solution remove your tube from the bath and let it cool down to room temperature. Once reached, place your tube into ice bath to further cool it down. Keep it on ice for 5 minutes and then filter it off using Hirsch funnel. Dry your product in the oven (TAs will set the oven temperature) and keep it for 10 min in there. Estimate the recrystallization yield.

Product characterization

Take your recrystallized product and record IR spectrum. Record the m.p. of your product as well. The m.p. apparatus should be operated in a range of 80 -150 °C. Your TA will set it up for you.

What is expected on the report

All standard lab report sections apply. Please see chapter 7 for details. More specifically, the following items are also required:

Introduction

Provides background information on the theoretical problem: Importance of aldol condensation reaction and its variants in organic chemistry. Provide examples and specific literature citations.

Results and discussion

Please to remember to reference all your spectra/images/tables in the text. Do not forget to make figure captions.

Results:
- Report the theoretical, obtained and recovery (recrystallization) yields. Show your calculations in your notebook (attached pages).
- Report IR spectra analysis (report your data in a usual table format), draw structure of your compound on all your spectra
- Report IR analysis of starting materials. Please analyze the spectra and include the results in your laboratory report (spectra available on Canvas). Attached this page to your lab report.

Discussion:

- Discuss similarities/differences between product and reagents. <u>Attach the original spectra at the end of your report</u>.
- Discuss your data by comparing it with literature values.
- What is the evidence that your product is a single geometric dibenzalacetone isomer not a mixture of isomers? Explain.

Conclusion(s)

Summarize the main features of the report, the objectives, findings and conclusions. You briefly explain any possible sources of error relevant to your results. Have you successfully performed the experiment? Why/why not? Was your synthesis/purification/analysis successful?

References

Please cite any references in ACS format. Remember to cite every source that helped you. Citation of other college/common websites are forbidden as they are not the valid source of information. DO NOT cite this manual, other courses' websites, only original works! Only primary citation sources such as journals and books will give you a full credit.

Report submission

Your complete lab report must include
1. Hard copy of your lab report & online submission.
2. Original pages from your lab notebook. Pages cannot be loose. You must staple/bind them before submission.
3. Attach original IR/NMR spectra and original pages from your lab notebook to a hard copy report.

Please pay attention to report deadlines. See Canvas for details.

Solvent extraction

Purpose

The purpose of this experiment is to demonstrate how liquid extraction can be applied for separation of complex organic mixtures. Liquid extraction combined with pH manipulation is the basis for acid-base extraction, which enables for separation of acidic, basic and natural compounds.

Number of laboratory sessions: 1

Background information

Mixtures of compounds can be separated in many ways. In organic chemistry liquid extraction, apart from filtration is one of the most useful techniques used for product purification or isolation. General overview of solvent extraction technique is covered in chapter 4.

Organic compounds can be (among many other categories) classified as acids (A), bases (B) and neutral compounds (N). These properties can also be used to purify them using a technique known as acid-base extraction. The fundamental theory behind this technique is that salts, which are ionic, tend to be water-soluble while neutral molecules tend not to be.

By manipulation of compound's protonation state, it is possible to separate them and isolate them from the mixture. Here is an example:

Benzoic acid is a simple aromatic carboxylic acid (see figure 39). Benzoic acid's solubility in water at room temperature is approximately 3.5g/L while solubility in diethyl ether is around 40 g/L. To be able to extract that acid efficiently using water we would have to convert free acid into its salt using for example NaOH. Solubility of sodium benzoate in water is approximately 630 g/L.

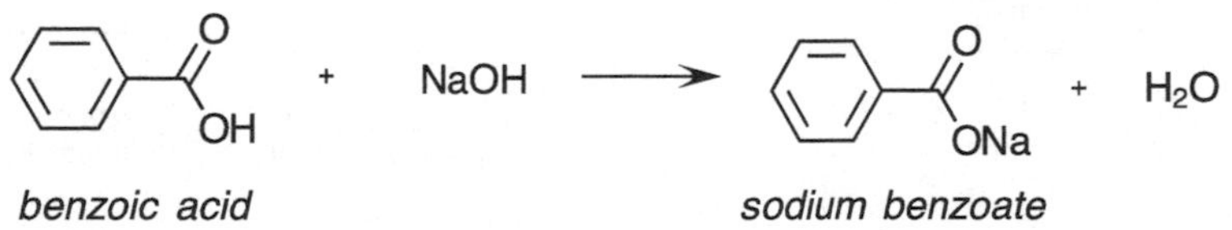

Figure 39. Benzoic acid and its salt formation upon reaction with strong base.

Sodium benzoate can be then easily separated from the organic mixture, using separatory funnel and later after acidification (conversion from salt to free acid) precipitated out and filtered off. Here is the flowchart depicting this acid-base extraction (Figure 40):

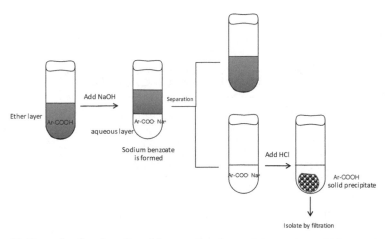

Figure 40. Example of carboxylic acid separation from mixture using acid-base extraction.

Analogously to the example above, it is possible to separate and isolate each acid, base and neutral compound from the mixture. Different separation routes, depending if starting point is acid or base addition are depicted on Figure 41. Isolation of the substance can be achieved using either – filtration or solvent evaporation. This depends on what is more convenient to perform.

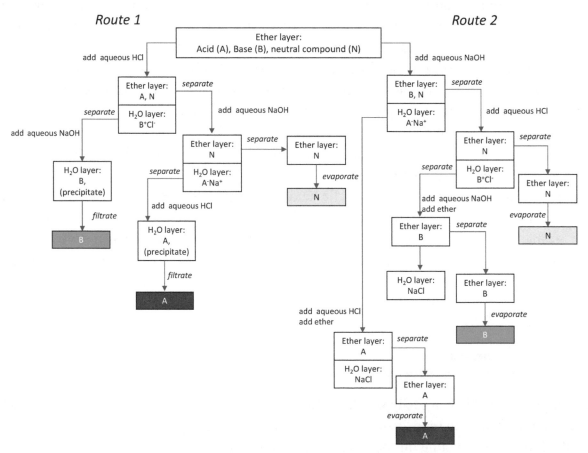

Figure 41. Acid-base extraction routes. Route 1 starts with addition of acid (HCl), while route 2 starts with addition of base (NaOH).

Compare the two routes. Note that every mixture component (except neutral compound) can be either precipitated from aqueous solution and isolated by filtering or after addition of another portion of ether separated from aqueous layer and after ether evaporation, recovered in solid form.

Pre-lab preparation

In your lab notebook, prepare the following:
1. Write acid-base reactions using NaOH/HCl and your acidic/basic compounds.
2. Hand written table of chemicals that include physicochemical data for **all** chemicals used (see chapter 6).
3. No flowchart is required for this pre-lab.

In the laboratory

You will have to weigh 50 mg of each component: acid (benzoic acid), base (4-nitroaniline) and neutral compound (9-fluorenone). All compounds, abbreviated A, B, N, need to be transfer to the same 1.5 mL microcentrifuge tube.

Next, TA will assign you your expected extraction route. See Figure 41 for a general flowchart. As you perform your experiment, please record all your steps in flowchart, directly into your lab notebook. At the end of the laboratory you will turn it in to your TA.

After separation of your mixture you are expected to perform a TLC analysis to verify the quality of your separation.

Main chemicals used in this laboratory exercise are:
- 9-fluorenone
- benzoic acid
- 4-nitroaniline
- 5% NaOH solution
- 5% HCl solution
- diethyl ether

Experimental procedure: stock solution preparation

Transfer your mixture from a centrifuge tube to large test tube. To the same tube, using graduated cylinder add 5 mL of diethyl ether (under the hood). Cap your tube and mix it using vortex mixer until all substances dissolve completely. Next, using Pasteur pipette transfer 3 droplets of that solution back to provided microcentrifuge tube. Cap it and set aside for further TLC analysis at the end of the extraction.

Having prepared starting solution of your mixture you are ready for separation. Follow instructions provided by TA regarding your assigned extraction route.

Experimental procedure: acid-base extraction

In this experiment, you will perform several addition, separation and/or filtration steps, depending on your route. Please label all your separated fractions! Common procedures for acid-base extraction are as follow:

- *Addition of aqueous NaOH*

To your tube add 2 mL of NaOH solution using calibrated Pasteur pipette. If you are adding NaOH to previously acidified solution you must add 3 mL of NaOH to make sure that your solution is not neutral. Two-phase system should be present. Stir it using vortex mixer for a 30-60 sec. Vent carefully. After the separation of layers, transfer ether layer to a separate tube.

- *Addition of aqueous HCl*

To your tube add 2 mL of HCl solution using calibrated Pasteur pipette. If you are adding HCl to previously alkalized solution you must add 3 mL of HCl to make sure that your solution is not neutral. Two-phase system should be present. Stir it using vortex mixer for a 30-60 sec. Vent carefully. After the separation of layers, transfer ether layer to a separate tube.

- *Addition of ether*

To your tube add 2 mL of diethyl ether. Stir it using vortex mixer for a 30-60 sec. Vent carefully. After the separation of layers, transfer ether layer to a separate tube.

- *Layer separation*

Wait until two-phase system is observed. Placing tube on ice for several minutes may help separation process. Separate layer by removing it with Pasteur pipette. Transfer it to a separate tube.

- *Filtration*

Prepare Hirsch funnel filtration setup. Filter-off precipitate. Wash precipitate twice with 1 mL of ice-cold distilled water. Air dry it. Weigh dry product and calculate percent recovery.

- *Evaporation*

To your tube containing ether layer add ~200 mg of anhydrous sodium sulfate. Wait couple of minutes. Filter that solution using Pasteur pipette equipped with cotton filter to another tube or Erlenmeyer flask. Under the hood, using slow stream of compressed air concentrate the sample. Solid product should be present. Weigh dry product and calculate percent recovery.

Having separated your mixture into individual components, prepare their solutions for TLC. If your samples are solid prepare their solutions by dissolving ~10 mg in 1 mL of diethyl ether. You may also want to perform the TLC analysis from final ethyl layer fractions. Spot samples on provided TLC plate (Figure 42), develop it using 20% EtOAc/hexanes as solvent system and under UV lamp mark all spots. Calculate R_f values of your individual components – acid, base and neutral compound. Analyze your separated compounds A, B, N and discuss your results.

Figure 42. TLC analysis of separated mixture components. M - mixture, A -acid, B-base, N-neutral compounds isolated by acid-base extraction.

What is expected on the report

All standard lab report sections apply. Please see chapter 7 for details. More specifically, the following items are also required:

Introduction

Provides background information on the theoretical problem: acids, bases and neutral compounds in organic chemistry. How are they defined? Give example of a very strong organic acid and base (draw structures).

Results and discussion

Please to remember to reference all your spectra/images/tables in the text. Do not forget to make figure captions.

> *Results:*
> - Turn-in your lab notebook pages containing flowchart made in the laboratory at the end of your experiment.

- Report recovery yields. Show your calculations in your notebook (attached pages).
- Report TLC analysis, including all R_f values (report your data in a usual table format). Redraw TLC plate using Chemdoodle.

Discussion:
- Discuss performed extraction process, including difficulties/observations made during experimentation.
- Discuss extraction yields and quality of your mixture separation based on TLC analysis.

Conclusion(s)

Summarize the main features of the report, the objectives, findings and conclusions. You briefly explain any possible sources of error relevant to your results. Have you successfully performed the experiment? Why/why not? Was your purification/analysis successful?

References

Please cite any references in ACS format. Remember to cite every source that helped you. Citation of other college/common websites are forbidden as they are not the valid source of information. DO NOT cite this manual, other courses' websites, only original works! Only primary citation sources such as journals and books will give you a full credit.

Report submission

Your complete lab report must include
1. Hard copy of your lab report & online submission.
2. Original pages from your lab notebook. Pages cannot be loose. You must staple/bind them before submission.

Please pay attention to report deadlines. See Canvas for details.

9. APPENDIX

Common units

In chemistry, SI units and metric system are used.

Measurement	SI Unit	Conversion Factors
Length	Meter (m)	1 m = 100 cm 1 cm = 10 mm 1000 mm = 1 m 1 cm = 0.3937 inches (in) 1 in. = 2.54 cm 1 angstrom (A) = 10^{-10} m
Mass	Kilogram (kg)	1 kg = 1000 g 1000 mg = 1 g 1000 mg = 1 g 1 kg = 2.205 pounds (lbs) 1 lb = 453.6 g 1 amu = $1.6605402 \times 10^{-24}$ g
Volume	Cubic meter (m^3)	$1 cm^3 = 1 mL$ 1000 mL = 1 L 1 liter (L) = $10^{-3}\,m^3$ $1\,in^3 = 16.4\,m^3$ 1 liter (L) = 1.057 quarts (qt)
Density	d	density = g/mL or kg/L
Mole	m	6.0221367×10^{23} atoms/mol
Temperature	Kelvin (K)	0 K = -273.15 Celsius (C) 0 K = -459.67 Fahrenheit (F) F = (9/5) C + 32 C = (5/9)(F - 32)
Molecular Weight	MW (of atomic weights of a molecular formula)	MW = g/mole
Formula Weight	FW (of atomic weights of a chemical formula)	FW = g/mole
Time	Second (s or sec)	1 minute (min) = 60 s 1 hour (hr) = 60 min 1 day (d) = 24 hr 1 day (d) = 86,400 s

Calculations

SI prefixes

Prefix	Symbol	Factor	Example
mega-	M	10^6	1 mega Dalton (MDa) = 10^6 Da
kilo-	k	10^3	1 kilogram (kg) = 10^3 g
deci-	d	10^{-1}	1 decimeter (dm) = 0.1 m
centi-	c	10^{-2}	1 centimeter (cm) = 0.01 m
milli-	m	10^{-3}	1 milligram (mg) = 10^{-3} g
micro-	μ	10^{-6}	1 microgram (μg) = 10^{-6} g
nano-	n	10^{-9}	1 nanometer (nm) = 10^{-9} m
pico-	p	10^{-12}	1 picogram (pg) = 10^{-12} g
femto-	f	10^{-15}	1 femotometer (fm) = 10^{-15} m

Calculation of the efficiency of reactions

If you are to perform an experiment, you have to know your reaction. You should be able to write it down and balance it. Once it is done, you can calculate how much of the product you should expect to obtain (theoretical yield). Next, after you isolate your pure product you can estimate the real amount of product obtained (reaction yield). To be able to calculate the efficiency of your reaction procedure you will compare it to the theoretical yield. This number, expressed as a percentage yield is one of the most important parameters used in practical organic chemistry.

Limiting reagent

The limiting reagent in a reaction is the reactant added to the reaction vessel in the fewest number of moles, after taking into account the stoichiometry of the reaction equation. There are two formulas necessary to calculate number of moles (n) of reactants:

$$n = \frac{m}{M} \ [moles] \qquad\qquad d = \frac{m}{L} \ [\frac{g}{mL} \ or \ \frac{mg}{\mu L}]$$

where d is the density of the compound if it is in liquid form.

Theoretical Yield

The theoretical yield is the maximum weight or quantity (in grams) of product that can be expected to be formed from a reaction. The theoretical yield is used to calculate percentage yield. The theoretical yield cannot be calculated until the limiting reagent for a reaction has been determined.

Reaction yield

The reaction yield (also called the actual yield) is the weight (in grams) of pure product obtained from the reaction.

Percentage yield

Percentage yield (% yield) describes the efficiency of the reaction. It is calculated according to the formula:

$$Percentage\ yield = \frac{actual\ yield}{theoretical\ yield}\ x\ 100\%$$

There are several steps needed for calculation of percentage yield:

Step 1   *Write the molecular formulas and determine molecular weights for reactants and products.*
Step 2   *Determine the number of moles of each of the reactants.*
Step 3   *Convert moles to molar equivalents if necessary by looking at stoichiometry of reaction.*
Step 4   *Determine the limiting reagent = maximum number of moles of product formed.*
Step 5   *Convert moles of product to grams of product = theoretical yield.*
Step 6   *Solve for % yield using the equation provided above.*

Recovery yield

To describe the efficiency of recovery of the product during product purification (e.g. recrystallization), the recovery yield is calculated according to the formula:

$$Recovery\ yield = \frac{recovered\ amount}{staring\ amount}\ x\ 100\%$$

Infrared absorption bands and corresponding molecular motions found in common functional groups

Wavenumber (cm⁻¹)	Assignment and molecular motion
	ALKANES
2960	Methyl symmetric C–H stretching
2930	Methylene asymmetric C-H stretching
2870	Methyl asymmetric C–H stretching
2850	Methylene symmetric C–H stretching
1470	Methyl asymmetrical C–H bending
1465	Methylene scissoring
1380	Methyl symmetrical C–H bending
1305	Methylene wagging
1300	Methylene twisting
720	Methylene rocking
	ALKENES
3100 – 3000	=C–H stretching
1680-1600	C=C stretching
1400	=C–H in-plane bending
1000 – 600	=C–H out-of-plane bending
	ALKYNES
3300-3250	≡C–H stretching
2260-2100	C≡C stretching
700-600	≡C–H bending
	AROMATICS
3100 – 3000	C–H stretching
2000 – 1700	overtone and combination bands
1600 – 1430	C=C stretching
1275 – 1000	In-plane C–H bending
900 – 690	Out-of-plane C–H bending

Wavenumber (cm⁻¹)	Assignment and molecular motion
3600	**ALCOHOLS AND PHENOLS**
3550 – 3500	Alcohol O–H stretching
1300 – 1000	Phenol O–H stretching
	C–O stretching
1100	**ETHERS**
	C–O–C stretching
	ALDEHYDES AND KETONES
2900 – 2700	Aldehyde C–H stretching
1740 – 1720	Aliphatic aldehyde C=O stretching
1730 – 1700	Aliphatic ketone C=O stretching
1720 – 1680	Aromatic aldehyde C=O stretching
1700 – 1680	Aromatic ketone C=O stretching
	ESTERS
1750 – 1730	Aliphatic C=O stretching
1730 – 1705	Aromatic C=O stretching
1310 – 1250	Aromatic C–O stretching
1300 – 1100	Aliphatic C–O stretching
	CARBOXYLIC ACIDS
3300 – 2500	O–H stretching
3300	C=O stretching
1430	C–O–H in-plane bending
1240	C–O stretching
930	C–O–H out-of-plane bending
	ANHYDRIDES
1840-1800	C=O stretching
1780-1740	C=O stretching
1300-1100	C–O stretching

ACYL HALIDES

1810-1800	C=O stretching

AMINES

3335	N–H stretching
2780	N–CH$_2$ stretching
1615	NH$_2$ scissoring, N–H bending
1360-1250	Aromatic C–N stretching
1210-1020	Aliphatic C–N stretching
850-750	NH$_2$ wagging and twisting
715	N–H wagging

AMIDES

3360 – 3340	1° Amide NH$_2$ asymmetric stretching
3300 – 3250	2° amide N–H stretching
3190 – 3170	1° amide NH$_2$ symmetric stretching
1680 – 1660	1° amide C=O stretching
1680 – 1640	2° amide C=O stretching
1650 – 1620	1° amide NH$_2$ bending
1560 – 1530	2° amide N–H bending, C–N stretching
750 – 650	2° amide N–H wagging

NITROGEN-BASED GROUPS

2260 – 2240	Aliphatic nitrile C≡N stretching
2240 – 2220	Aromatic nitrile C≡N stretching
2180 – 2110	Aliphatic isonitrile –N≡C stretching
2160 – 2120	Azide N≡N stretching
2130 – 2100	Aromatic isonitrile –N≡C stretching
1690 – 1620	Oxime C=N–OH stretching
1680 – 1650	Nitrite N=O stretching
1660 – 1620	Nitrate NO$_2$ asymmetric stretching
1560 – 1530	Aliphatic nitro compound NO$_2$ asymmetric stretching
1540 – 1500	Aromatic nitro compound NO$_2$ asymmetric stretching
1450 – 1400	Azo compound N=N stretching
1390 – 1370	Aliphatic nitro compound NO$_2$ symmetric stretching
1370 – 1330	Aromatic nitro compound NO$_2$ symmetric stretching
965 – 930	Oxime N–O stretching
870 – 840	Nitrate N–O stretching
710 – 690	Nitrate NO2 bending

HALIDES

1300–1000	C–F stretching
800–400	C–X stretching (X = F, Cl, Br or I)

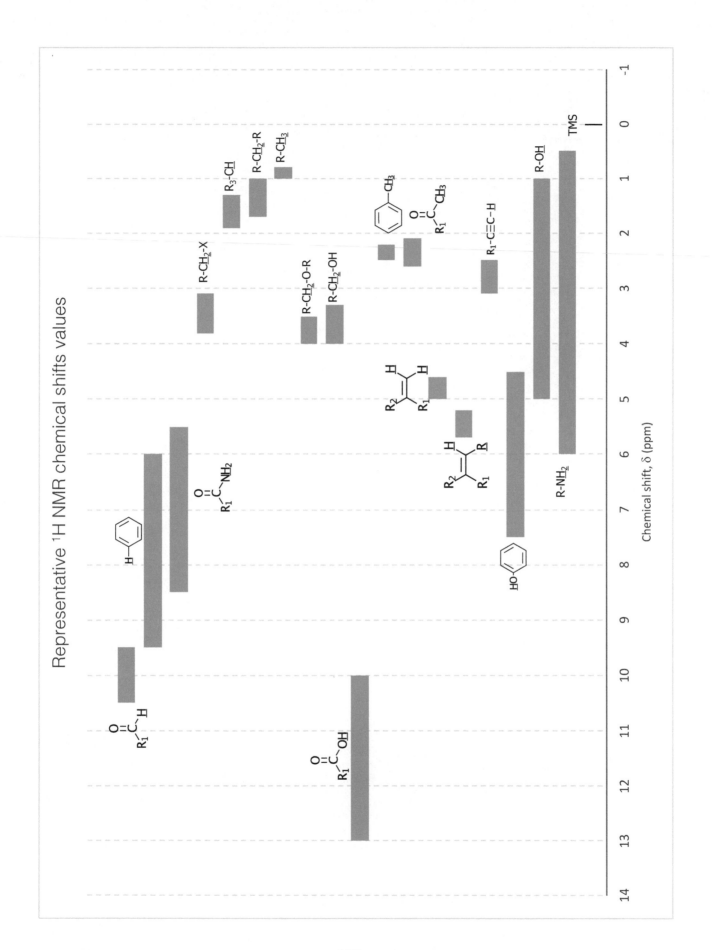

Representative ¹H NMR chemical shifts values

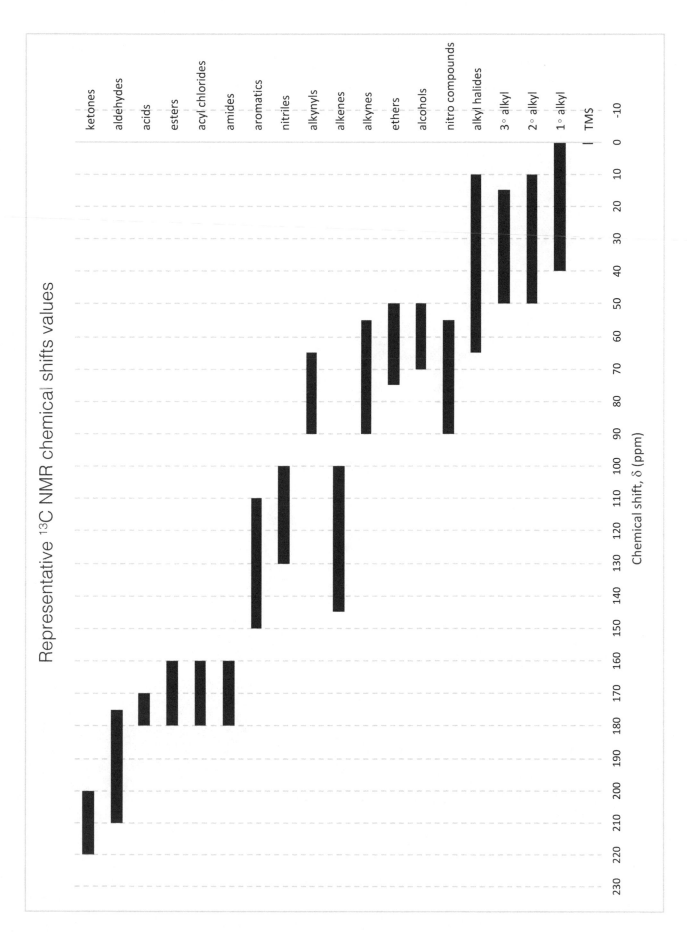

Representative ^{13}C NMR chemical shifts values

Chemical shift, δ (ppm)

ketones
aldehydes
acids
esters
acyl chlorides
amides
aromatics
nitriles
alkynyls
alkenes
alkynes
ethers
alcohols
nitro compounds
alkyl halides
3° alkyl
2° alkyl
1° alkyl
TMS

FUNCTIONAL GROUPS IN ORGANIC CHEMISTRY

A functional group is a group of atoms within the organic molecules responsible for characteristic chemical reactions of those molecules.

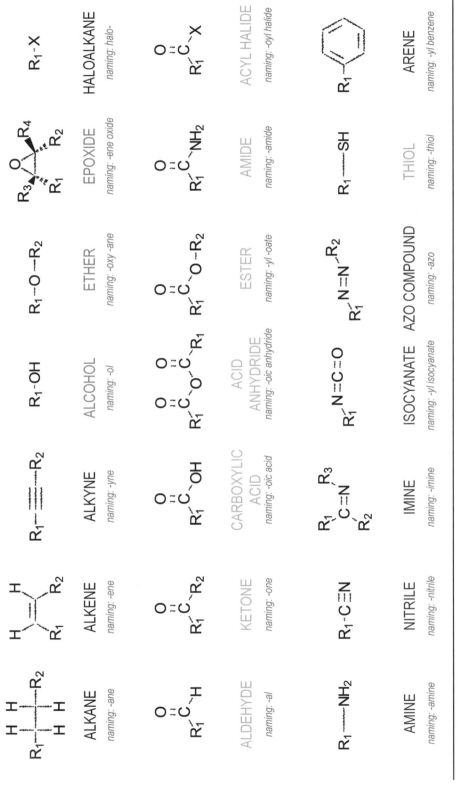

ALKANE
naming: -ane

ALKENE
naming: -ene

ALKYNE
naming: -yne

ALCOHOL
naming: -ol

ETHER
naming: -oxy -ane

EPOXIDE
naming: -ene oxide

HALOALKANE
naming: halo-

ALDEHYDE
naming: -al

KETONE
naming: -one

CARBOXYLIC ACID
naming: -oic acid

ACID ANHYDRIDE
naming: -oic anhydride

ESTER
naming: -yl -oate

AMIDE
naming: -amide

ACYL HALIDE
naming: -oyl halide

AMINE
naming: -amine

NITRILE
naming: -nitrile

IMINE
naming: -imine

ISOCYANATE
naming: -yl isocyanate

AZO COMPOUND
naming: -azo

THIOL
naming: -thiol

ARENE
naming: -yl benzene

● **HYDROCARBONS**   ● OXYGEN-BASED   ● CARBONYL COMPOUNDS   ● NITROGEN-BASED   ● SULFUR-BASED   ● *AROMATIC*

"X" represents halogen atom: F, Cl, Br, I
"R" represents the rest of the molecule